D0919807

MELODRAMAS and FARCES
for
YOUNG ACTORS

Melodramas and Farces for Young Actors

by

EARL J. DIAS

WEST BEND PUBLIC LIBRARY

Publishers   PLAYS, INC.   *Boston*

CAUTION

The plays in this volume are fully protected by copyright law. All rights including motion picture, recitation, television, public reading, radio broadcasting, and rights of translation into foreign languages are strictly reserved.

NOTICE FOR AMATEUR PRODUCTION

These plays may be produced by schools, clubs, and similar amateur groups without payment of a royalty fee.

NOTICE FOR PROFESSIONAL PRODUCTION

For any form of non-amateur presentation (professional stage, radio or television), permission must be obtained in writing from the publisher. Inquiries should be addressed to PLAYS, INC., 8 Arlington Street, Boston 16, Massachusetts.

Library of Congress Catalog Card Number: 56-11516

FOR EDITH

CONTENTS

MELODRAMAS and FARCES
for
YOUNG ACTORS

Way, Way Down East

Characters

BEFORE RISE: *The* NARRATOR *appears on the apron of the stage and holds up his hands for silence.*

NARRATOR: How do you do, folks? Welcome to our play. What you're about to see is a real, old-fashioned melodrama, the kind that Grandpa and Grandma used to enjoy so much. Of course, times have changed since their day, so we don't want you to take matters too seriously.

Like all rip-roaring melodramas of the not-so-gay nineties, this one has a beautiful heroine, a handsome hero, and a thoroughly nasty villain. The villain will feel very much at home if you hiss and boo him whenever the

3

spirit moves you. The hero and heroine, naturally, will welcome your applause.

The main idea is for you to sit back, relax, and have a good time. I want to assure you at the outset that virtue will be rewarded and villainy foiled.

So—let's turn back the clock a good sixty years or more and get on with the play. Will the ladies please remove their hats and the gentlemen refrain from chewing tobacco? Thank you.

And, by the way, I'll just sit on the side of the stage here where I can enjoy myself, too. (*He goes to left and sits on a chair.*) I may make an occasional comment for your edification and enlightenment.

Have fun! And now we go to the living room of the Ludlow farmhouse, with Mother and Father Ludlow on the premises.

SCENE 1

TIME: *Early evening.*

SETTING: *The living room of the Ludlow farmhouse, somewhere in New England.*

AT RISE: HEPZIBAH LUDLOW, *the mother, is seated at left of table. She is darning a pair of her husband's socks. EZEKIEL is pacing the floor restlessly. Occasionally, he goes to the window and looks out. Then he shakes his head, sighs, and resumes his pacing.*

HEPZIBAH: You're restless, Ezekiel. Mighty restless.

EZEKIEL: Our lovely daughter, Lily, should have returned by now. Ah, I hope that she has been favored by good fortune and that Banker Skinnem has agreed to lend us the money so that we can make the payment on our mortgage.

HEPZIBAH: We must trust in her and in Banker Skinnem's generosity. (*Sighing*) Ah, these are difficult times for us.

HENRIETTA (*Entering from left*): You folks havin' soup again tonight?

HEPZIBAH: Yes, I believe so, Henrietta.

HENRIETTA: Then what're you goin' to do for spoons?

EZEKIEL: Ah, woe is me!

HEPZIBAH: What's wrong, husband?

HENRIETTA: I guess he means there ain't but two spoons left in the whole house. You'll have to eat your vittles in relays.

HEPZIBAH (*Turning to her husband*): Ezekiel, you didn't!

EZEKIEL (*Hanging his head and sinking dejectedly into chair at right of table*): I sold the rest of our silverware down at the village yesterday, Hepzibah. Had to get some money to buy feed for the chickens. (*He clasps his head in his hands.*)

HEPZIBAH (*Rises, comes over to him, strikes a pose, and places her hand on his shoulder*): Don't be dejected, Ezekiel. Some women would blame you for our ills, but I shall remain by your side through thick and thin. Come what may, I am your faithful wife.

NARRATOR (*Rises from chair*): Now isn't that touching? Let's give this good, faithful soul a round of applause. (*He leads audience in applause and sits down.*)

HENRIETTA: Them's real lovely words, ma'am. (*She wipes her eyes with her apron.*) Makes a body want to weep. Well, I'll get that soup ready. Too bad about the spoons though. (*She exits as* HEPZIBAH *returns to her chair and resumes her darning.*)

EZEKIEL (*Rising and speaking as he goes to window*): It would be a blessing if Lawyer Tedious J. Impossible, who holds our mortgage, would give us an extension.

HEPZIBAH: Be of better cheer, Ezekiel. Perhaps he will. He has always seemed to be a generous man.

NARRATOR: That's a good one. Wait until you see this Tedious J. Impossible. He's a real dyed-in-the-wool villain!

EZEKIEL: But, lo, our lovely daughter, Lily, returns from her errand of mercy. Let us hope fervently that she is the bearer of good tidings.

HEPZIBAH: Amen to that. (LILY, *the young, beautiful, rosy-cheeked daughter of the household, enters. She is breathless and seems disconsolate.*)

LILY: Hello, dear Mother. Hello, good Father.

EZEKIEL: Your tidings, child.

LILY: Alas, good Father, the words stick in my throat.

HEPZIBAH: You mean—

LILY: Banker Skinnem has refused our request.

EZEKIEL (*Sinking into chair again and taking head in hands*): Alas, alas, one woe comes upon the other.

LILY: Sorrow seems to follow us.

EZEKIEL: The crops have failed.

HEPZIBAH: Dobbin, our faithful horse, is lame.

LILY: Matilda, the cow, has the croup.

EZEKIEL: And my rheumatiz is bothering me again. (*Sighing*) But we must take the bitter with the sweet.

HEPZIBAH: But, indeed, the hand of misfortune is laid heavily upon us. And the mortgage is due tomorrow night at six.

LILY: And yet, dear Mother and good Father, there is one bright ray of hope glimmering on the dark horizon.

HEPZIBAH: Is there, child? Pray tell us what it is.

LILY: Ronald may yet save us.

EZEKIEL: Ah, Ronald. He is a splendid young man.

HEPZIBAH: So good—

LILY (*Sighing*): And so handsome.

EZEKIEL: And so true.

HEPZIBAH: But how may Ronald save us from losing the roof over our heads?

LILY: Ronald, bless his dear heart, has invented a new kind of safety valve for use on locomotives. He has written to the President of the Railroad, Bertram J. Moneybags, and if Mr. Moneybags buys the invention, Ronald will lend us the money for the mortgage.

HEPZIBAH: What an unselfish fellow!

EZEKIEL: But will he know in time to help us?

LILY: Let us pray that he will. (*Goes to window*) But lo, Ronald is here now.

HEPZIBAH: And let us hope he brings good news. (RONALD, *the young, handsome hero, enters at center*.)

LILY: Ronald!

RONALD (*Taking her hand and looking adoringly into her eyes*): Lily!

EZEKIEL (*Rising quickly and coming to* RONALD): What's the news, boy?

RONALD (*Coming down to table*): Alas, sir, I have heard nothing.

EZEKIEL (*Going to* HEPZIBAH *and placing hand on her shoulder*): I fear, good wife, that we shall soon go over the hill to the poorhouse.

HEPZIBAH: But I shall stand by you to the end, Ezekiel.

NARRATOR: What a woman! A little applause, please! (*He rises, leads audience in applause, and sits down.*)

RONALD: Perhaps I have raised my hopes too high. My invention, which sounded so practicable on paper, may not be workable at all. At least, I have as yet heard nothing from Bertram J. Moneybags.

LILY (*Placing a hand on his arm*): Oh, say not so, Ronald. All of us have faith in you—supreme faith.

RONALD: Bless you for those words.

EZEKIEL (*Goes to window and looks out*): Ah, here comes Lawyer Tedious J. Impossible now. Let us hope he will grant us a few more days of grace.

HEPZIBAH: Amen to that. (TEDIOUS J. IMPOSSIBLE, *the villain, enters. He bows to all of them.*)

IMPOSSIBLE: Ah, my good friends, a good evening to you all. (*To* HEPZIBAH *as he bends over to kiss her hand*) You are looking well, my dear Mrs. Ludlow. (*Going to* LILY *and pinching her cheek*) And the fair Lily—how fetching you look, my child.

EZEKIEL: Good evening to you, Mr. Impossible.

IMPOSSIBLE (*Twirling moustache*): And now to a painful subject. Please believe that it grieves me to the heart to mention the matter, for Tedious J. Impossible is known far and wide as a man of mercy and a sensitive soul.

NARRATOR: What a hypocrite!

IMPOSSIBLE: But business, alas, is business. Do you have the money for the mortgage?

EZEKIEL: Not yet, but—

IMPOSSIBLE (*Twirling moustache*): No money at all?

HEPZIBAH: Alas, sir, not at present. But if you could give us more time—

IMPOSSIBLE: My dear Mrs. Ludlow, if I had only myself to consult, I should be delighted to do so. But I have my business to consider. It cuts me to the quick to have to say this, but unless the money is forthcoming by six o'clock tomorrow night, I shall have to foreclose. (*Takes out handkerchief and wipes a supposed tear from his cheek*) Though it will hurt me enormously to do it. (*He comes downstage center and speaks, in an aside, to audience.*) Little do they know that Bertram J. Moneybags, the railroad president, wishes to buy their south pasture for five thousand dollars. His company wishes to extend its tracks. Once I have the farm, the money from the sale will be mine. (*Twirls moustache*) Heh! Heh! Heh!

NARRATOR (*Rising from chair*): Have you ever seen a more miserable cur? Let's hiss him thoroughly—with a few boos thrown in for good measure. (*He leads hissing and booing and then sits down.*)

LILY: But, sir, if Ronald sells his invention, we may have the money soon.

IMPOSSIBLE: But me no buts, my dear. (*He pinches her cheek again.*) Ronald is a fine fellow (*He bows to* RONALD, *as* HENRIETTA *enters from left*), but business is business. (*He goes to* MRS. LUDLOW *and kisses her hand once more.*) Dear Mrs. Ludlow, try to forgive me for the pain I have brought you, but I must do my duty.

HENRIETTA: What lovely manners!

IMPOSSIBLE: Thank you, my dear.

RONALD: But, sir, surely a few days extension will make little or no difference.

IMPOSSIBLE: Please. No more of this. I am a sensitive soul, and you'll have me weeping.

HEPZIBAH: It will be over the hill to the poorhouse for us.

IMPOSSIBLE: Fear not, Mrs. Ludlow. The poorhouse is warm and quite comfortable. And you will have many companions. (*Aside to audience*) Heh! Heh! Heh! It's a cold, damp place, and the inmates freeze there. Ah, well, business is business, and tomorrow at six, this place will be mine. (*Twirling moustache*) And the five thousand dollars from Bertram J. Moneybags for the south pasture will be mine. (*Goes to door*) Now I must end this painful mission.

Till tomorrow night at six, then. (*Menacingly*) I go, but I shall return. Heh! Heh! Heh! (*Exits*)

NARRATOR: Don't let him get away without a few hisses. (*Leads audience in demonstration*)

HEPZIBAH: Alas, all is lost.

HENRIETTA: Mr. Impossible seems like such a nice man, though. He has the loveliest manners.

RONALD: And yet, there is something about the man that is not quite sincere.

LILY: Do you really think so, Ronald?

RONALD: I do, indeed. But now I must be off. Who knows, by now there may be a letter awaiting me from Bertram J. Moneybags. Be of good cheer, Lily, your Ronald is not yet beaten.

LILY (*Rapturously*): Oh, Ronald.

RONALD (*At door, center*): Farewell for now. May the dawn bring new hope.

NARRATOR: What a brave young fellow, one in a million. A round of applause, please. (RONALD *exits.*)

HENRIETTA: Well, the soup's ready. And I washed them two spoons. Who's going to eat first?

LILY: You eat first, good Mother and dear Father. I find I have little appetite at present.

HEPZIBAH: Very well, child. Come, Ezekiel. We must keep body and soul together no matter how much woe descends upon us.

EZEKIEL (*Following her to door, left, followed by* HENRIETTA): Yes, Hepzibah. (*Sighing*) We must take the bitter with the soup.

CURTAIN

* * * *

Scene 2

TIME: *Late afternoon, the next day.*
SETTING: *The woods near the south pasture of the Ludlow farm.*
AT RISE: LILY *enters, basket on arm, and comes downstage center.*

LILY: I came here to the woods near our south pasture this afternoon in search for blueberries. We need something to stock our lean larder, for Henrietta's soup is gone. Alas, that it should come to this—we are on the brink of poverty. And still no word from Ronald. I trust that Bertram J. Moneybags will buy his invention. Then all would be well, the mortgage could be paid, and I could share wedded bliss with Ronald. How wonderful he is! How manly and how generous! (*Putting hand to ear*) But, hark, I hear voices. And one of them sounds familiar. I shall hide behind this bush lest someone discover my shame in searching for food. (*She hides.*)

NARRATOR: A familiar voice, indeed. It's that loathsome Tedious J. Impossible with his horrible partner, William P. McNasty. Listen—and hiss, too. (TEDIOUS J. IMPOSSIBLE *and* McNASTY *enter.*)

IMPOSSIBLE: So you see, my dear McNasty, that this south pasture will be a veritable gold mine for us. Moneybags wants it badly and has offered five thousand dollars for it. The Ludlow family—Heh! Heh! Heh!—does not know of the offer. (*Poking* McNASTY *in the ribs*) A pretty piece of business, hey McNasty. Five thousand dollars trickling beautifully into our own pockets. (*Twirling moustache*) It's a wonderful world. And tonight at six, the farm is ours, with this delightful and profitable south pasture. Heh! Heh! Heh!

McNasty: You're a shrewd and clever man, Tedious. What you've done warms the cockles of my heart. And it's the poorhouse for the Ludlows, hey?

Impossible (*Laughing maliciously*): Indeed, it is. Sad, isn't it? Heh! Heh! Heh!

Lily (*Bursting from her hiding place*): You cads! You unspeakable cads!

Impossible: Gad, what's this?

McNasty: Discovered!

Lily: I heard all. Oh, I did not know there could be such evil in the world! For shame, sirs, for shame! I shall return home at once to tell good Mother and dear Father the truth!

Impossible (*Grabbing her arm*): So, my proud beauty, you'll return home, will you? (*Laughs*) Not on your life, you won't. I shall seal those pretty lips.

Lily (*Frightened*): Unhand me, sir. What do you mean?

Impossible: No chit of a girl outwits Tedious J. Impossible. This will be your last day on earth, my proud beauty. (Lily *struggles to free herself, but* McNasty *grasps her other arm.*)

McNasty: There'll be no escape, my girl.

Lily: I'm not your girl. I belong to Ronald.

Impossible: You'll never see that handsome young stick again, I assure you. Come, McNasty, we'll soon be rid of this wench. (*They drag* Lily, *screaming, offstage at left.*)

Narrator: My goodness, what a fix the fair Lily is in! But courage, folks. All will yet be well.

CURTAIN

* * * *

SCENE 3

TIME: *A few minutes later.*

SETTING: *The railroad tracks.*

AT RISE: LILY *is tied to the tracks, a gag in her mouth.* IMPOSSIBLE *and* MCNASTY *stand near her.*

IMPOSSIBLE: So, my proud beauty, I have you in my power. (LILY *struggles.*) Heh! Heh! Heh! Your struggles will avail you nothing. The bonds are tight and the train will soon be here.

MCNASTY (*Glancing at his pocket watch*): The train should be here in about ten minutes.

IMPOSSIBLE: Ten minutes to live, my dear. How sad. (*Takes out handkerchief*) Your plight moves me to tears. (*Wipes his eyes*) I shall probably hate myself in the morning, but— business is business. Heh! Heh! Heh! Have you any last request, my dear? Any message for the dear ones you are leaving behind? (*Twirls moustache*) But I quite forgot, you cannot talk, can you? How sad! How very sad! (*Wipes eyes again*)

MCNASTY: We had better be leaving here, Tedious. It would not do to be seen in this area.

IMPOSSIBLE: How right you are, McNasty. (*To* LILY) Well, my dear, a fond farewell. We are not likely to meet again. Heh! Heh! Heh! Come, McNasty. (*He twirls moustache, as they exit laughing.* LILY, *left alone on the stage, continues to struggle vainly.*)

NARRATOR: Oh, dear, things look black for Lily. (*Looking at watch*) And the train is due in exactly six minutes. But wait—I hear footsteps. (RONALD *suddenly enters breathlessly.*)

RONALD: Lily! I heard voices as I passed nearby. (*He quickly unties her and removes her gag.*)

LILY: Oh, Ronald. Thank heaven you are here! (*He clasps her in his arms.*)

RONALD: Who is responsible for this horrible outrage? No, let me guess. Was it Tedious J. Impossible?

LILY: And that terrible McNasty.

RONALD: They shall pay dearly for this!

NARRATOR: Applause, please.

RONALD: I have good tidings for you. Bertram J. Moneybags is on his way. He will arrive early tonight and has promised to talk with me at your home. He is interested in my invention.

LILY: Oh, Ronald! How wonderful! And I have tidings for you. Mr. Moneybags wishes to purchase our south pasture so that the railroad tracks can be extended. I overheard Tedious J. Impossible and William P. McNasty discussing it. That is why Impossible was so anxious to foreclose the mortgage, and that is why he planned my extinction.

RONALD: In any event, all will be well. And as for Impossible, we shall have our revenge for his dastardly action. Keep silent about all this until tonight. Then we shall have an unpleasant surprise for Tedious J. Impossible or my name is not Ronald Fitzwilliam.

LILY: Oh, Ronald, you're wonderful! What a lucky girl I am!

RONALD: No, it is I who am lucky, and I shall devote my life to being worthy of you. (*They embrace.*)

NARRATOR: A magnificent speech! Applause, please. And that's the end of the scene.

CURTAIN

* * * *

SCENE 4

TIME: *That evening, a few minutes before six o'clock.*
SETTING: *Same as Scene 1.*
AT RISE: MRS. LUDLOW *is in her accustomed chair at left of table, darning socks. Her husband is seated at right of table.* RONALD *is standing at window with* LILY. BERTRAM J. MONEYBAGS, *a prosperous-looking and kindly railroad president, is seated on sofa.*

EZEKIEL: Mr. Moneybags, you have brought joy to our poor home.

HEPZIBAH: Think of it, five thousand dollars! It is a veritable fortune to poor folk such as we. Why, we'll be able to pay off the mortgage, repair the chicken house, and get a doctor for Matilda.

MONEYBAGS: Matilda?

EZEKIEL: Matilda's our cow. She's had the croup.

HEPZIBAH: Poor thing.

MONEYBAGS: And all this you have told me about Tedious J. Impossible's villainous scheme has, indeed, opened my eyes. I have corresponded with him, and he always seemed such a gentlemanly fellow.

RONALD: And yet there has always been something about the man that struck me as not being quite sincere.

LILY: Oh, Ronald, you're such a wonderful student of human nature.

MONEYBAGS: And a mighty ingenious inventor, too.

RONALD: Thank you, Lily. Thank you, sir.

MONEYBAGS: This Impossible should be arriving about six, you say?

EZEKIEL: Yes, the mortgage is due at that time.

MONEYBAGS: And he knows nothing of your daughter's timely escape?

EZEKIEL: Nothing at all.

RONALD: His consternation will be a joy to see.

HEPZIBAH: And Constable Wickwire and his assistant are hiding behind the house, so that if Impossible attempts to escape, he will be snatched.

MONEYBAGS: Splendid! This was worth coming down from New York for!

LILY: New York! The magic city! How I should love to see it!

MONEYBAGS: And so you shall, my dear, when Ronald and you are wed.

LILY: What do you mean?

MONEYBAGS: I have offered Ronald a splendid position in our New York office. We need young men of his industry and ambition.

LILY: Oh, Ronald, how magnificent!

RONALD: But, lo, here at hand is Tedious J. Impossible!

LILY: I shall hide myself in the kitchen. (*She exits left as* RONALD *comes down to sofa where he sits beside* MONEYBAGS. TEDIOUS J. IMPOSSIBLE *enters, center, and comes downstage.*)

IMPOSSIBLE: Good evening, my friends. (*He kisses* HEPZIBAH's *hand.*) As always, you are looking well, Mrs. Ludlow. (*Looking around*) But where is the fair Lily? When she is absent, a little sunshine goes out of all our lives. (*To* RONALD) And how is our young inventor? Blooming, I trust. (*Nodding toward* MONEYBAGS) I don't believe I know this gentleman.

EZEKIEL: Time for introductions later.

IMPOSSIBLE: Later, ah yes. After all, this is a night for business—sad business, I assure you. I assume you do not have the money for the mortgage.

HEPZIBAH: You assume we do not.

IMPOSSIBLE: Unless—Heh! Heh! Heh!—your ship has come in since yesterday. But, (*Sighs*) 'tis seldom indeed in this sad, sad world that fortune finds us.

EZEKIEL: You are right, alas. Seldom does good fortune come—even to those who most deserve it.

IMPOSSIBLE: And I say to you, from the bottom of my heart, that no family is more deserving than yours. Oh, how it pains me! If only I could spare you this misery. But I must do my duty.

HEPZIBAH: We all must do our duty.

IMPOSSIBLE: I would even give up my own proud position of trust in this community to save you, if I may say so.

HEPZIBAH: You may say so.

IMPOSSIBLE: But business, alas, is business. Ah, if misfortune should ever strike me, I trust that I will be able to bear its blows with the courage and fortitude shown by your little family. For when an ill wind blows, then is a man's true character exposed.

RONALD: Then prepare to be exposed, Impossible. You are an unmitigated scoundrel!

IMPOSSIBLE (*Glaring*): What's that!

RONALD: An unmitigated scoundrel and a would-be murderer! (*Goes to door, left*) Lily!

IMPOSSIBLE: Sir, I resent your words! (*Suddenly realizing the name* RONALD *has just called*) Lily? (LILY *appears suddenly at left, followed by* HENRIETTA.)

LILY: Yes. It is I. As you can see, your dastardly scheme has failed. And I owe my life to dear Ronald. (*She goes to* RONALD *and takes his hand.*)

IMPOSSIBLE: Gad! Foiled!

HENRIETTA: And to think I was so took in by his lovely manners!

EZEKIEL: Your wickedness is known to us all. We trusted you, but you have proved to be a viper, creeping poisonously into our home.

IMPOSSIBLE (*Suavely*): My dear Mr. Ludlow, certainly you must realize I was indulging my sense of humor. Everything was in fun—all in fun. Surely, you do not think that a man of my kind heart and sensitive soul would actually wish to harm a hair of this lovely girl's head.

MONEYBAGS: You're smooth as oil, Impossible, but you're not convincing anyone. You're a miserable cur, and we all know it.

IMPOSSIBLE: I take no such talk from a stranger.

MONEYBAGS: We're not strangers. We've corresponded frequently. I am Bertram J. Moneybags.

IMPOSSIBLE: Moneybags!

MONEYBAGS: And in addition to being a cur, sir, you're a down-right thief—trying to deprive these good people of the money that is rightfully theirs.

IMPOSSIBLE (*Backing gradually toward door, center*): It's all a mistake. You are all misjudging me. I'm an honest man, a sensitive soul—(*He turns suddenly and tries to rush out of the door. RONALD rushes to him, they grapple, IMPOSSIBLE is thrown to the floor, and RONALD sits on his chest.*)

LILY: Oh, well done, Ronald!

HENRIETTA: My, isn't Ronald the strong one, though!

MONEYBAGS: Your life of crime is at an end, Impossible.

HEPZIBAH: Constable Wickwire is awaiting you outside, Mr. Tedious J. Impossible.

IMPOSSIBLE: Curses!

EZEKIEL: And it will be the jail for you.

HEPZIBAH (*Sarcastically*): But it's so warm and comfortable there.

EZEKIEL: Take him outside to Constable Wickwire, Ronald. (RONALD *drags* IMPOSSIBLE *to his feet and to door, center*)

IMPOSSIBLE: Curses! Curses on all of you! I'll be revenged!

NARRATOR: Now, folks, this is our last chance to give this nasty villain a really noisy send-off. Let's have some good and loud booing and hissing, please. (*He leads audience in a demonstration.* IMPOSSIBLE *shakes his fist at audience as he and* RONALD *exit.*)

EZEKIEL: At long last good fortune seems to be smiling on us.

LILY: Yes, dear Father, in every cloud there is a silver lining.

HEPZIBAH: We'd be mighty proud, Mr. Moneybags, if you'd share our simple evening meal with us.

MONEYBAGS: Why, thank you, ma'am.

HENRIETTA (*Coughs, and speaks in a stage whisper*): But, ma'am, we ain't got but two spoons.

EZEKIEL (*Laughing*): Fear not, Henrietta. Now that happiness and wealth have come to us, I shall go down to the village immediately and buy back our silverware.

HENRIETTA: Oh, blessed day!

HEPZIBAH: Amen to that! (RONALD *enters at center.*)

RONALD: He's safely delivered into the hands of the law.

LILY: You were wonderful, Ronald.

RONALD: And his evil partner, William P. McNasty, soon will be arrested, too.

EZEKIEL: We have much for which to be thankful.

HEPZIBAH: Our home restored—

EZEKIEL: Our silverware to be returned—

LILY: New York for Ronald and me—

RONALD: My invention a success—

EZEKIEL: But, above all, we have learned to take the bitter

with the sweet! (LILY *and* RONALD *embrace*, HEPZIBAH *and* EZEKIEL *put their arms affectionately about each other*, MONEY-BAGS *beams, and* HENRIETTA *does a little jig as the curtains close.*)

THE END

Production Notes

WAY, WAY DOWN EAST

Characters: 5 male; 3 female; narrator may be either male or female.

Playing Time: 25 minutes.

Costumes: Old-fashioned dress. Hepzibah, Lily and Henrietta all wear long skirts or dresses. Lily's dress should be colorful, while Hepzibah's and Henrietta's are dark-colored and very plain. Henrietta wears a large white apron. The men all wear suits of the 1890's period. Their costumes may be as elaborate as desired. Impossible and McNasty wear large moustaches.

Properties: Socks, darning equipment, handkerchief, basket, rope, gag, pocket watch, wrist watch.

Setting: Scenes 1 and 4: Living room of farmhouse, somewhere in New England. The entire room has a somewhat shabby appearance. At center is a plain, wooden table on which are a large family Bible and a vase of flowers. To left and right of table are chairs. At downstage right is a rather dilapidated sofa. There is a door at left, leading into the kitchen. At center is a door which leads onto front porch. At left and right of this door are windows. Hanging on the wall is a framed sampler which reads, "God Bless Our Happy Home." Scene 2 may be played in front of the curtain, or greens and cardboard trees may be used to give the effect of a woods on stage. Scene 3 may also be played in front of curtain, in which case

Lily should be dragged on stage by McNasty and Impossible and tied to the railroad tracks. If Scene 3 is done on the stage the set could be the same as that for Scene 2. *Lighting:* No special effects.

Feudin' Fun

Characters

Paw Hogwash, *a typical hillbilly*
Lulu Belle, *his beautiful daughter*
Grandpaw Hogwash
Mamie Crackers, *a kind-hearted neighbor*
Zeke Hogwash, *a fellow of sixteen*
Ronald Candy, *a handsome stranger*
Maw Fudge, *a typical hillbilly woman*
Hector Fudge, *her sixteen-year-old son*

Scene 1

Time: *Late one morning*
Setting: *The Hogwash cabin.*
At Rise: Paw Hogwash *is seated on box at right of table.* Mamie Crackers, *a buxom woman of middle age, is placing a bandage on his arm.* Lulu Belle, *a pretty girl of seventeen, is watching. The only decent piece of furniture is downstage left—a rocking chair in which* Grandpaw Hogwash *is seated, eyes closed, battered straw hat on head, rocking silently.*

Mamie: Looks like only a flesh wound, Paw Hogwash. Them Fudges aren't as good marksmen as they used to be.

Paw: Hector Fudge caught me unawares. I was down by

the crick huntin' up dandelion greens when the sneakin' critter winged me.

MAMIE: Well, you got him good last week. That was a nasty wound you gave him on his ankle. I was over there takin' care of it.

LULU BELLE: You're an angel of mercy, Mamie Crackers. You have been a comfort and blessing to all of us in the hills since Maw passed to the Great Beyond.

PAW: Yep, we're sure grateful, Mamie.

LULU BELLE: Indeed, we are.

MAMIE: Shucks, Paw, and shucks, Lulu Belle, it's nothin' really. A body ought to do what he can for his fellow critters, and I was always one for tendin' to the sick and the sufferin'. But I'll tell you somethin', Paw Hogwash, I'm a-gettin' mighty fed up patchin' up Hogwash wounds and Fudge wounds. You people been feudin' ever since I can remember.

PAW: Them Fudges is all snakes. As Grandpaw used to say in the days when he was talkin', "There's no good Fudge but a dead Fudge."

MAMIE: Them's harsh words, Paw Hogwash.

PAW: But them's true words, Mamie Crackers.

MAMIE (*Nodding toward* GRANDPAW): How is Grandpaw Hogwash these days?

PAW: Poorly. For nigh onto ten years, he's been a-sittin' and a-rockin' in that chair. He don't say nothin', and he don't do nothin'—except eat.

MAMIE: He always was a mite lazy.

PAW: It's not so much lazy he is as sensible. I recollect he used to tell me when I was a boy, "Son, when you can sit, sit; and when you can get flat on your back, get there. There's no use in rushin' around in this world."

LULU BELLE: The true lady or gentleman always appears to be relaxed. He or she will at all times maintain an air of calm and graciousness.

MAMIE: My, you sure do say things real purty, Lulu Belle.

PAW: That's what comes of an eddication. Lulu Belle was in school for almost two years—up at Badger Crick.

MAMIE: Badger Crick! Say, that's a real big place!

PAW: Sure is. Must be all of two hundred people livin' there. Too big for me. I can't stand all the noise and excitement of them big places.

LULU BELLE: The reason why my talk is so elegant, Mamie Crackers, is that at school our only book was "Mrs. Moonmush's Phrasebook for Young Ladies." Published in 1855. I memorized it.

MAMIE: My, it must be wonderful to have a brain like yours. (To PAW) There now—that bandage ought to hold for a while—at least until you get winged again by one of them Fudges.

PAW: Blast their danged hides!

LULU BELLE: Now, Paw, a gentleman never gives vent to his most deeply felt emotions.

MAMIE: What started all the feudin' between the Hogwashes and the Fudges?

PAW: It's a right complicated story, Mamie. Began in Great-Great-Grandpaw Hogwash's day. Great-Great-Grandpaw was a great hand for flowers. Went out pickin' daisies one day and picked some over on the other side of our property. Great-Great-Grandpaw Fudge seen him and shot him right through the leg. Fudge claimed that Grandpaw Hogwash was on Fudge property. Since then, we've been a-layin' for each other. There's no good Fudge but a dead Fudge.

LULU BELLE: To maintain tensions among neighbors, as Mrs. Moonmush says in her phrase book, is an act bordering on the discourteous.

PAW: That Mrs. Moonmush never knew such sneakin' hounds as the Fudges. If she had, she'd never have written them words. (ZEKE HOGWASH, LULU BELLE's *brother, enters up center.*)

ZEKE: Mornin', Mamie Crackers. Them Fudges wing you again, Paw?

MAMIE: Mornin', Zeke.

PAW: They got me again, son. But I'll be gettin' one of them before long.

ZEKE: There's no good Fudge but a dead Fudge.

PAW: Right, son, right. Truer words was never spoken.

ZEKE: There's a stranger wanderin' around near here. I seen him down near the crick.

PAW (*Taking his shotgun from table*): A stranger? It's not one of them mealy-mouthed Fudges, is it?

ZEKE: Don't look like one of them Fudges, Paw. It's not Maw Fudge, and it's not her son, Hector.

PAW: Hector's the one that winged me, blast his hide!

ZEKE: It's not any of 'em. Fact is I never seen this one before. He's a right good-lookin' young feller.

LULU BELLE: True hospitality is one of the most pleasant signs of good breeding. We should welcome the stranger.

ZEKE: Just because I said he was good-lookin', hey, Lulu Belle?

LULU BELLE: And a brother should always display toward his sister the utmost respect and the sincerest affection.

ZEKE: That's what Mrs. Moonmush says, I reckon.

LULU BELLE: She does, indeed. (*There is a knock at door up center*)

PAW (*Rising, shotgun in hand*): If that's one of them low-born Fudges, I'll blast him to kingdom come.

MAMIE: Control yourself, Paw Hogwash. (PAW *goes to door and opens it. In the doorway stands* RONALD CANDY, *a good-looking young fellow of twenty, dressed in city clothes and wearing shoes.*)

RONALD (*Glancing nervously at gun*): How do you do, sir?

PAW: What's your business, young feller?

RONALD: I am a stranger and alone, seeking the favor of a night's rest before I resume my wanderings.

LULU BELLE: One should comfort the stranger and offer him the hospitality of the hearth.

RONALD: Those words! They sound familiar. Where have I heard them?

LULU BELLE: I quote "Mrs. Moonmush's Phrasebook for Young Ladies," sir.

RONALD: Mrs. Moonmush!

ZEKE: You know her, stranger?

RONALD: No, but during my schooling in Purple Creek, on the other side of these hills, my chief book was "Mr. Moonmush's Phrasebook for Young Gentlemen."

LULU BELLE: Indeed, I have heard of it. Mr. Moonmush wrote for young gentlemen a book similar to that which his wife wrote for young ladies. (*Advancing toward* RONALD *and holding out her hand*) I am Lulu Belle Hogwash, and I am delighted to make your acquaintance, stranger.

RONALD (*Shaking her hand*): I am Ronald Candy. Shaken by the tensions of modern civilization, I have been indulging in a walking tour to gain back my peace of mind.

LULU BELLE: The habit of walking in the open air is a tonic for both young and old of either sex.

RONALD: That's exactly what Mr. Moonmush says.

LULU BELLE: So does Mrs. Moonmush.

MAMIE: Say, you young folks have plenty in common.

RONALD (*Gazing rapturously at* LULU BELLE): Indeed, we have.

MAMIE (*Coming to* RONALD *and shaking his hand*): I'm Mamie Crackers.

PAW (*Shaking his hand*): I'm Paw Hogwash.

ZEKE (*Shaking* RONALD'S *hand*): I'm Zeke Hogwash.

LULU BELLE: And there, in the rocking chair, is Grandpaw Hogwash.

RONALD (*Coming to* GRANDPAW *and holding out hand*): I'm delighted to meet you, sir. (GRANDPAW *gives no response, merely continues to rock*)

PAW: Don't expect Grandpaw to say nothin'. He hasn't talked for nigh onto ten years.

RONALD: How tragic! Is he ill?

PAW: No, there's nothin' really wrong with Grandpaw. He just don't believe in exertin' himself. Got a good appetite, though. Eats his three square meals a day and then some.

RONALD: Toward the aged, one should always comport oneself with the greatest of respect and the maximum of solicitude.

LULU BELLE: Mr. Moonmush?

RONALD: Yes.

LULU BELLE: Mrs. Moonmush says the same thing.

RONALD: He and his wife must have been kindred spirits— even as you and I.

LULU BELLE (*Somewhat flustered*): Oh, sir!

PAW: So you want a night's lodgin', stranger?

RONALD: I should appreciate it, Paw Hogwash.

PAW: Well, don't see no harm in givin' you bed and board for the night. Not much room in here, but we can bed you out in the shed.

RONALD: That will be most satisfactory.

ZEKE: The pig's been sleepin' in there, Paw.

PAW: Well, get her out for the night. Fresh air'll do her a heap of good.

ZEKE: I'll get her out now, Paw. (ZEKE *exits up center.*)

MAMIE: I'll be on my way, too. Old Mrs. Teablossom is feelin' poorly, and I promised to drop by.

LULU BELLE: You're an angel of mercy, Mamie Crackers.

MAMIE: As for you, Paw, keep out of the way of them Fudges. I'm gettin' low on bandages.

PAW: There's no good Fudge but a dead Fudge.

MAMIE: Maw Fudge says there's no good Hogwash but a dead Hogwash.

PAW: Maw Fudge is a sneakin' hyena of a woman with a stone where her heart ought to be!

MAMIE: Well, all I know is I'm right sick of all your feudin'. Goodbye, all. (MAMIE *exits center.*)

RONALD: I gather, sir, that you are not on good terms with the Fudge family.

PAW: We're not on any terms at all with them horse thieves.

LULU BELLE: Oh, Paw, how I wish we could stop this eternal bickering with the Fudges and live peacefully with them.

RONALD: True neighborliness is one of the hallmarks of the civilized lady or gentleman.

LULU BELLE: Mr. Moonmush?

RONALD: None other.

PAW: I'll live in peace with them Fudges only when Maw Fudge and that lyin' rascally son of hers, Hector, are pushin' up daisies. Well, stranger, I'll go out to see how Zeke is comin' with the pig. She's a mite stubborn at times. Likes to doze in the shed most of the day and night.

RONALD: Thank you, sir. (PAW *exits up center.*)

LULU BELLE: Is it not a sad situation, Mr. Candy?

RONALD: Please call me Ronald. When a young man and a young woman have obvious traits and interests in common, there is no reason why their relationship should not be on a first-name basis.

LULU BELLE: Does Mr. Moonmush say that?

RONALD: In his book, he mentions the matter no less than three times—surely an indication of his firm belief in the value of his advice.

LULU BELLE: Yes, (*Pausing*)—Ronald.

RONALD: The name becomes music when you say it.

LULU BELLE: Oh, Ronald!

RONALD: I seem to feel that Fate destined us to meet. Do you not have the same feeling, Lulu Belle?

LULU BELLE: Mrs. Moonmush says a young lady never should reveal her true feelings to a young gentleman with whom she has just become acquainted.

RONALD: But I feel that I have known you all my life.

LULU BELLE: And so do I. Oh, Ronald, I do think that Fate did arrange our meeting.

RONALD: Bless you for those words. (*Frowning suddenly*) And yet, there is something I must tell you. A gentleman should always be truthful and honorable toward the young lady of his affections.

LULU BELLE: But why do you frown, Ronald?

RONALD: Is it safe to reveal a deep secret in the presence of Grandpaw Hogwash?

LULU BELLE: Of course. Grandpaw will never hear. It is ten years since he has done anything except eat.

RONALD: So be it. Then, my secret is this. (*Dramatically*) I am not Ronald Candy. I am a Fudge.

LULU BELLE: A Fudge!

RONALD: Yes. My family moved from here when I was only

a baby. Recently, I have nursed a longing to see the place of my birth. Consequently, I journeyed here, but I did so with some misgiving for I had heard of the feud between the Fudges and the Hogwashes. But I determined to come and, if possible, to put an end to the feud.

LULU BELLE: But, how, Ronald?

RONALD: You will know very soon.

LULU BELLE: Oh, Ronald. How sad it is to learn that just when you and I have found each other, our families are the most bitter of enemies.

RONALD: Always remember—behind every cloud there is a silver lining.

LULU BELLE: And, as Mrs. Moonmush says, there is always a brighter tomorrow.

RONALD: Bless her. (PAW HOGWASH *and* ZEKE *enter up center.*)

PAW: The pig's out so you can move in any time, Mr. Candy.

ZEKE: Had a heap of trouble gettin' her carcass out of there, but we done it.

RONALD: Thank you for your hospitality.

PAW: Wasn't nothin' at all. Glad to help, young feller. (GRANDPAW HOGWASH *suddenly raises his head and points dramatically at* RONALD.)

GRANDPAW: That man's a Fudge. (PAW, ZEKE, *and* LULU BELLE *open their mouths in astonishment.* RONALD *is completely startled.*)

ZEKE: He spoke, Paw!

PAW: I heard him! Question is, did I hear right? What was that, Grandpaw?

GRANDPAW (*Pointing again at* RONALD): That man's a Fudge! (*Obviously exhausted by this Herculean effort,* GRANDPAW *resumes his former position, hat over eyes, and begins to rock as though nothing has happened.*)

PAW: Grab the critter, Zeke! (ZEKE *grasps* RONALD. PAW *takes up his shotgun and aims it at* RONALD'*s head.*) Now speak, boy, or you'll be spattered all over this here floor!

LULU BELLE: Paw, please!

PAW: Stay out of this, girl. This here is man's work.

RONALD: I shall not lie to you, Paw Hogwash. I am, indeed, a Fudge, although I have not lived in this vicinity since I was a baby.

PAW: You must be Lem Fudge's boy.

RONALD: I am.

PAW: I recall Lem all right. Winged him good in the shoulder one day.

RONALD: His shoulder still pains him in damp weather.

PAW: Good.

LULU BELLE: Paw!

PAW: Get them ropes from the shed, Zeke.

ZEKE (*Releasing* RONALD): Right, Paw.

LULU BELLE: You're not going to tie him up, Paw!

PAW: Tyin's tame to what I'm goin' to do to him. There'll be a real cosy shootin' in the mornin'. I'll send Zeke to get Cousin Clootie and Aunt Henrietta and Uncle Zeph and Cousin Dilly. We'll have us a real family party— just like the old days.

LULU BELLE: Paw, you couldn't be so cold-blooded as that!

PAW: There's nothin' cold-blooded about it. There's no good Fudge but a dead Fudge. And this one's no exception. (ZEKE *enters with rope in his hand*)

ZEKE: I got me them ropes, Paw.

PAW: Good work, son. Tie his hands and his ankles. We'll let him sleep on the floor tonight, and we'll take turns watchin' the mangy critter. We're havin' a shootin' to-morrow mornin', son. Give us a chance to see all our relatives. I want you to go up in the hills to get Cousin Clootie, Aunt Henrietta, Uncle Zeph, and Cousin Dilly.

ZEKE: It sure will be a real pleasure, Paw. There's no good Fudge but a dead Fudge. (ZEKE *begins to tie* RONALD'S *hands behind him.*)

RONALD: Paw Hogwash, I protest. I came here seeking only peace.

PAW: You'll get plenty of peace tomorrow mornin', Fudge.

RONALD: But I have information I came to give you.

PAW: Put a gag on him, Zeke. I don't want no Fudge words pollutin' the air of our house. (ZEKE *takes a checkered handkerchief from his pocket and ties a gag around* RONALD'S *mouth.*)

ZEKE: That'll keep him quiet.

LULU BELLE: Oh, Ronald, I am so ashamed of my family for what they are doing! (RONALD *tries to answer, but only muffled sounds come out.*)

PAW: Get on the floor, Fudge. (ZEKE *takes* RONALD *by the shoulders and presses him to the floor. He quickly ties together* RONALD'S *ankles.*)

ZEKE: That'll keep him safe for the night, Paw.

PAW: Reckon it will. And now off with you, Zeke. Tell the relatives to be here tomorrow mornin' round about nine. Let's hope it's a real nice day for the party. I'll keep my eye on the critter.

ZEKE: I'll be back afore sundown, Paw.

PAW: I'll be waitin', son. (ZEKE *exits up center.* LULU BELLE *goes to* GRANDPAW'S *chair and looks down at him.*)

LULU BELLE: Oh, Grandpaw Hogwash! How could you! (GRANDPAW *makes no response, but continues his rocking.*)

PAW: He seen his duty and he done it. Better go to your room, girl. This is man's work, this watchin' the Fudge

critter. There's no good Fudge but a dead Fudge. (LULU
BELLE *begins crying.* RONALD *emits smothered sounds, and*
PAW *continues to point the shotgun at* RONALD *as the curtain
falls.*)

*   *   *   *

SCENE 2

TIME: *Early the next morning.*
SETTING: *Same as Scene 1.*
AT RISE: RONALD, *still bound and gagged, is lying on the floor.*
PAW HOGWASH, *shotgun beside him, is seated at left of table.*
PAW *rises slowly, stretches his arms over his head, and yawns.*
He looks over at GRANDPAW *who, as always, is rocking silently,*
eyes closed, hat pulled down. PAW *chuckles. Then he goes to the*
door, opens it, and looks out.

PAW: It's goin' to be a mighty purty day. Sun's comin'
up over the hills and the flowers is bloomin'. Perfect day
for a shootin'. (*Muffled sounds come from* RONALD) When
Zeke come home last night, he was pleased—mighty
pleased. All the relatives is comin' later for the fun. (PAW
returns to his seat.) Yes, sir, this'll be a real fine day for all.
(*Chuckling*) Except you, of course, Fudge. There's no
good Fudge but a dead Fudge. (ZEKE *enters.*)

ZEKE: I been lookin' all over the place, Paw, but I can't
find hide nor hair of Lulu Belle.

PAW: You mean she's disappeared?

ZEKE: She's not anywhere hereabouts.

PAW: What could have become of the girl?

ZEKE: Don't look like her bed's been slept in, neither.
(MAMIE CRACKERS *enters.*)

MAMIE: Mornin', all. Came to take a look at that wound of yours, Paw Hogwash. (*Noticing* RONALD *on floor*) Say, what's all this?

PAW: That there Candy has turned out to be a Fudge. We're shootin' him today.

MAMIE: Paw Hogwash, have you gone plumb crazy? That's murder.

PAW: Killin' Fudges don't count as murder. Comes under the headin' of public improvements.

MAMIE: Where's Lulu Belle? I'm sure she's not in favor of all this.

ZEKE: Lulu Belle's not here.

MAMIE: Well, I'm tellin' you, you're an old fool, Paw Hogwash.

PAW: Names can't hurt me this mornin', Mamie Crackers.

MAMIE: At least, let me take the gag out of that poor boy's mouth.

PAW (*Menacingly*): Leave him alone, Mamie Crackers. I don't want no Fudge words spoken in this house. (LULU BELLE, *breathless, suddenly enters. She is carrying a piece of paper in her hand.*)

ZEKE: Where you been, Lulu Belle? I been combin' the place for you.

LULU BELLE: You'll learn soon enough. I have brought visitors with me, Paw.

PAW: Visitors? Oh, you mean Cousin Clootie, Aunt Henrietta, Uncle Zeph, and Cousin Dilly. Well, that's fine, girl. Bring 'em right in.

LULU BELLE: It isn't our relatives, Paw. (*She turns toward exit and motions those outside to come in.* MAW FUDGE, *a woman of about* PAW'S *age, enters, followed by her son,* HECTOR FUDGE, *who is about* ZEKE'S *age.*)

PAW: Maw Fudge! Hector Fudge! (*He grabs shotgun from*

table and levels it at them) This'll be the greatest mornin'
of my life. Three Fudges here all at once to meet their
Maker. (LULU BELLE *throws herself between* PAW *and the
two* FUDGES.)

LULU BELLE: A true lady should be willing to offer even her
life for righteous principles. Fire if you will, Paw, but I
shall die with them.

PAW: You out of your head, girl? Stand back so I can fill
them sneakin' Fudges full of holes.

MAMIE: You're an old lunatic, Paw Hogwash!

LULU BELLE (*Holding the piece of paper aloft*): Wait, Paw!
Wait until you hear what I have here.

MAW FUDGE: Listen to her, you old hog.

HECTOR: We don't like this any more'n you do, but right's
right.

PAW: I never thought I'd live to see the day when blasted
Fudges would be talkin' under my roof. Out of the way,
girl!

LULU BELLE (*Holding her ground*): This paper is the property
of Ronald, who lies there, alas, a victim of his honest
heart and loving kindness. Ronald found the paper in
the county records. It states that the property on which
Great-Great-Grandpaw Hogwash was picking daisies
when Great-Great-Grandpaw Fudge shot him did not
belong to the Fudges.

PAW: Just what I always said! Them sneakin', dirty, lyin',
rascally Fudges never had a leg to stand on.

LULU BELLE (*Dramatically*): And neither did the property
belong to the Hogwash family.

MAW FUDGE: So put that in your pipe and smoke it, Paw
Hogwash.

HECTOR: And I hope it chokes you.

PAW: You mean neither us or them Fudges owned the land?

LULU BELLE: I do. The land belonged and still does to the Bluenose family up at Badger Creek.

PAW (*Sinking to seat*): Then we all been wrong all these years?

LULU BELLE: Always remember, Paw, that the true lady or gentleman should be willing to admit when she or he is in error.

PAW: It's a mighty blow to a man's pride, girl.

ZEKE: Guess I'd better untie this Fudge critter. (ZEKE *removes gag from* RONALD *and unties his arms and legs.*)

RONALD (*Rising stiffly*): How happy I am that all is now well.

MAMIE: What's botherin' me is how you found out about all this, Lulu Belle.

LULU BELLE: Very early this morning I crept into this room and discovered that both Paw and Grandpaw were sleeping. I wished, of course, to release dear Ronald from his bonds, for a young lady should always practice tenderness and sympathy toward those around her.

MAMIE: Mighty well spoken, Lulu Belle.

LULU BELLE: Thank you, Mamie Crackers.

RONALD: Lulu Belle was unable to loosen me, for the ropes were too tight and no knife was at hand.

ZEKE: I hid all them knives when I seen how you and Lulu Belle seemed to be makin' eyes at each other.

RONALD: However, Lulu Belle was able to remove my gag. As a result, I was able to tell her of the paper which I was prevented yesterday from displaying. She then decided to go to bring back Maw Fudge and Hector in the hope of settling once and for all this terrible feud. She replaced my gag, so that no one would suspect what had happened.

MAW FUDGE: Seems like we both been wrong, Paw Hogwash. I'm willin' to shake and forget. (*She comes to* PAW,
hand outstretched. PAW *rises and hesitates.*)

MAMIE: Be a man, Paw Hogwash.

PAW: It's not easy to shake hands with a Fudge after what
we all been through. (*Bravely*) But I'll do it. (*He shakes
her hand, then looks closely at her.*) You know, Maw, you're
not a bad-lookin' woman.

MAW FUDGE: And you're not so hard on the eyes either,
Paw Hogwash.

PAW: It's been mighty lonely around here since Maw Hogwash died.

MAW FUDGE: And things has been pretty lonesome for me
since Paw Fudge passed on.

MAMIE: Zack Summers, the travelin' preacher, will be
around these parts tomorrow. Why don't you folks get
hitched?

HECTOR: Say, that's a good idea, Maw.

RONALD: A very good idea, Paw Hogwash, for I feel that
I soon shall be taking your lovely daughter away from
you.

MAMIE: You mean you two is gettin' hitched, too?

RONALD: If Lulu Belle will have me, I shall devote the rest
of my life to her comfort and happiness.

LULU BELLE: Oh, Ronald!

RONALD: And Paw Hogwash, please believe that you are
not so much losing a daughter as gaining a son.

PAW: You for this marriage business, Maw Fudge?

MAW FUDGE: Well, seein' how the feud's over, what do we
have to lose? No use keepin' up hard feelin's when both
our families have been wrong all these years.

PAW: Then we'll do it!

LULU BELLE: Oh, Paw. How happy you make me! The

marriage tie is, indeed, a bond that brings strength and happiness to those who enter it.

RONALD: Mrs. Moonmush?

LULU BELLE: Yes, Ronald.

MAMIE: One good thing I know is that I won't have to be bindin' up any more Hogwash and Fudge wounds. I was gettin' mighty tired of it.

RONALD: I have a splendid idea. We shall have a double wedding tomorrow, for, as Mr. Moonmush so aptly states, double bliss is double joy.

MAW FUDGE: That we will.

HECTOR: I'm goin' home to get my gee-tar. We'll have us a big party right now with dancin' and singin' and eatin'.

MAW FUDGE: You bet we will.

PAW: Some of my folks from over the hills will be comin' too. They was comin' for another purpose, but a party's a party. We'll have us a real shindig.

LULU BELLE: A family celebration is the warmest form of civilized good will.

RONALD: And in the bosom of the family, one may partake of the greatest joy in life.

PAW: Yes, sir, we'll have us a rootin', tootin', roarin' shindig! (*He grasps* MAW FUDGE *about the waist and begins to do a lively dance with her. Suddenly* GRANDPAW HOGWASH *rises from his rocker, shouts "Wheee!", grabs* MAMIE, *and begins to dance with her. The others are frozen momentarily in astonishment. Then* RONALD *clasps* LULU BELLE *in his arms.*)

RONALD: After the darkness comes the light.

LULU BELLE: Where love reigns, there happiness is also. (*They, too, join in the dance as the curtain falls.*)

THE END

Production Notes

Feudin' Fun

Characters: 5 male, 3 female.

Playing Time: 25 minutes.

Costumes: Paw Hogwash wears overalls, a ragged shirt, and is barefoot. Grandpaw, Zeke, and Hector are similarly dressed. Grandpaw wears a battered straw hat, and may have a long white beard. Mamie and Maw Fudge wear old, faded gingham dresses, perhaps bonnets, and are barefoot. Lulu Belle is more neatly dressed, but her clothes are still shabby. She too is barefoot. Ronald wears city clothes and shoes.

Properties: Bandage, shotgun, jug, rope, checkered handkerchief, piece of paper (a title or deed).

Setting: Hillbilly cabin room. At center is a large wooden table on which is a shotgun and jug. Boxes serve as chairs, and there is a dilapidated sofa. Down left is a decent-looking rocking chair, in which Grandpaw sits.

Lighting: No special effects.

The Sands of Time

Characters

KATHY REYNOLDS
SUE REYNOLDS, *her older sister*
JACK SPRAGUE, *Kathy's boy friend*
DAN HOWARD, *Sue's fiancé*
MRS. REYNOLDS
UNCLE DENNIS

TIME: *Early afternoon.*
SETTING: *The Reynolds living room.*
AT RISE: KATHY REYNOLDS, *about sixteen, is seated before the fireplace idly turning the pages of a magazine.* UNCLE DENNIS, *a portly, jolly-looking gentleman of middle age, is standing and looking out window, left.*

UNCLE DENNIS: That rain is really coming down now, Kathy. Gosh, there's been no let-up all day.

KATHY: Well, thank goodness, it's Saturday. At least, I didn't have to trudge to school in this downpour. I'd have been drenched by the time I got there. (*Returns to her magazine, then looks up suddenly*) Uncle Dennis?

UNCLE DENNIS (*Turning away from window and coming to couch where he sits*): Yes?

KATHY (*Slowly and thoughtfully*): Don't you think that older

41

men are far more interesting to girls than just plain high school boys?

UNCLE DENNIS (*Laughing*): Well, as an older man myself— and I do mean older—I suppose I ought to agree with you. But aren't you being a bit hard on just plain high school boys? You take young Jack Sprague, for example. I wouldn't call him plain at all. In fact, he's a mighty good-looking young fellow.

KATHY: Young is right! He's only sixteen! And he's so immature!

UNCLE DENNIS: If I remember correctly, you're only sixteen yourself, aren't you?

KATHY: But that's different. I think I was older at ten than Jack is right now. Mr. Sanders, my English teacher, says I have an unusually mature outlook on life.

UNCLE DENNIS: And what gives him that idea?

KATHY: My English themes, of course. He says they're thoughtful and show emotional balance.

UNCLE DENNIS: By golly, Kathy, my high school English teacher never told *me* anything like that. She was a little, fiery old lady who wielded a red pencil with zeal and zest. In fact, she had more energy than a carload of vitamin pills. "Dennis," she used to say to me, "your spelling is absolutely the worst I've encountered in forty years of teaching!" (*Chuckling*) She was probably right, too.

KATHY: You've got company there. Mr. Sanders says Jack's spelling is simply horrible. It's a shame, too, because he has a good mind—when he wants to use it.

UNCLE DENNIS (*Ironically*): But, of course, he's immature.

KATHY: Oh, you probably think I'm exaggerating, but I'm not. He has absolutely no interest in the finer things of life.

UNCLE DENNIS: Such as—?

KATHY: Such as the ballet, for example. I tried to get him to go with me last week when that ballet company appeared here. But he wouldn't. He says ballet is sissy stuff. Now, I ask you, isn't that immature?

UNCLE DENNIS: Well—

KATHY: And only yesterday in English class he uttered about the most immature remark I've ever heard. We're reading "Idylls of the King."

UNCLE DENNIS: I remember it well. King Arthur and Queen Guinevere, and Lancelot and Galahad.

KATHY: It's lovely and so romantic. You remember, though, how Elaine wasted away because Sir Lancelot didn't return her love?

UNCLE DENNIS: Very sad, indeed.

KATHY: Well, just when we got to the most romantic part —you remember, where Elaine's dead body is placed on a barge and floated down to Camelot—Jack raised his hand. And what do you think he said?

UNCLE DENNIS: Don't keep me in suspense.

KATHY: Now get this. He said, "Mr. Sanders, I think this Elaine was pretty dumb. What did she want to get all stirred up for, when this guy Lancelot is old enough to be her father. That girl needed to get around more." Now, I ask you. Isn't that positively revolting?

UNCLE DENNIS: Perhaps Jack is just a realist.

KATHY: He's a dope! He has absolutely no soul, no finer feelings.

UNCLE DENNIS: Don't be so hard on the boy.

KATHY (*Rises and goes to table, right, where she places the magazine she has been reading*): Well, I'll just bet that Dan Howard wouldn't say anything like that.

UNCLE DENNIS: Dan's a lot older than Jack.

KATHY: He's not so old.

UNCLE DENNIS: He must be thirty or more.

KATHY (*Coming to couch and sitting*): Now you sound just like Jack. He laughs at me for admiring Dan so much. Jack says Dan's best years are behind him. But I think Dan's wonderful. He's just like Lancelot.

UNCLE DENNIS: And are you going to be another Elaine, Kathy?

KATHY: I wouldn't mind being Elaine for him.

UNCLE DENNIS: Correct me if I'm wrong, but isn't the remarkable Dan engaged to your sister Sue?

KATHY: Yes—and I don't think she appreciates him.

UNCLE DENNIS: That's not a very nice thing to say.

KATHY: I don't mean to be unfair or unkind, but she does take him too much for granted. And he's so wonderful and so sensitive. (MRS. REYNOLDS *enters from left. She is a pleasant-looking, rather matronly woman. She comes to center.*)

MRS. REYNOLDS: What are you two discussing so seriously?

UNCLE DENNIS: Life, love, and the pursuit of happiness. (MRS. REYNOLDS *goes to window and looks out.*)

MRS. REYNOLDS: What a nasty day! I'm glad I've no clothes on the line. Oh, here comes a friend of yours, Kathy.

KATHY: Who?

MRS. REYNOLDS: It's Jack, I think. He's so bundled up in that raincoat of his that it's hard to make out his features.

KATHY: Golly! What in the world does he want?

MRS. REYNOLDS: You might sound more hospitable.

UNCLE DENNIS: Your daughter seems to prefer more mature men.

MRS. REYNOLDS: Don't tell me she's mooning about Dan again. I wish you'd try to be more sensible, Kathy. Your obvious hero worship makes Dan uncomfortable, and I don't think Sue likes it either.

KATHY: You can't control love.

MRS. REYNOLDS: Fiddlesticks!

KATHY: And please, I beg you, don't tell me I'm the victim of puppy love. There's no such thing.

MRS. REYNOLDS: There is in this house.

UNCLE DENNIS: Now, ladies! Ladies! (*The doorbell rings.* MRS. REYNOLDS *answers the door and admits* JACK SPRAGUE, *a breezy, good-looking boy of sixteen.*)

MRS. REYNOLDS: Hello, Jack. My, you look soaked. Let me take your coat.

JACK: It *is* wet out. (MRS. REYNOLDS *holds out her hand for his coat. He removes it and hands it to her.*) Thanks, Mrs. Reynolds.

MRS. REYNOLDS: I'll hang this up where it can dry. (*She exits left.*)

JACK (*Coming down to couch*): Hi, Uncle Dennis. Hello, Kathy.

UNCLE DENNIS: How are you, Jack? (*Rises*) I think I'll get myself a cup of coffee. Need something to take the chill out of these old bones on a damp day like this. See you kids later. (*He exits left as* JACK *sits beside* KATHY *on couch. There is a complete silence for a minute or two.*)

JACK: What is this—a morgue?

KATHY: Very funny.

JACK: Well, for Pete's sake, you might at least say hello

KATHY: Hello.

JACK: What's wrong, anyway?

KATHY: I don't think you'd understand.

JACK: Why not try me out? After all, I'm not a moron.

KATHY: That's a matter of opinion, after yesterday.

JACK: What do you mean, "after yesterday"?

KATHY: I'm referring to that charming little episode in English class.

JACK (*Laughing*): Oh, you mean what I said about that dizzy Elaine.

KATHY: She wasn't dizzy.

JACK: Well, my gosh, I don't think it's very bright for a kid her age to carry a torch for a guy as old as Lancelot.

KATHY: You just about mortified me, that's all. Why, after class, Betty Linwood shook her head in sympathy, and she said to me, "I know just how you must feel, Kathy."

JACK: And just what did she mean by that?

KATHY: She knows that you and I have been going to the movies together and that you took me to the Halloween Hop. So she feels sorry for me—being so much in the company of such an insensitive person.

JACK: Phooey!

KATHY: And you can say phooey all you want, but it doesn't change things.

JACK (*Suddenly contrite*): Gosh, I'm sorry, Kathy. You know I didn't mean to hurt you, and I didn't come here to argue with you.

KATHY: Then just why are you here?

JACK: The same old thing. I still want you to go to the dance with me tonight.

KATHY: No.

JACK: But, for Pete's sake, why not? I can dance, can't I?

KATHY: Oh, yes, I'll say that for you. You can dance.

JACK: Well, then—?

KATHY: Let's just say the weather is too bad. I wouldn't want the rain to ruin my dress.

JACK: Please, Kathy—

KATHY: And if you really want to know, Dan and Sue have invited me to go to the movies with them.

JACK: You mean you'd give up a perfectly good dance just

to go and sit in a stuffy theater with your sister and her boy friend?

KATHY: Yes.

JACK (*Rising and beginning to pace the floor*): I suppose the real reason is that you're still crazy about Dan. And you know he's engaged to your sister, and he's far too old.

KATHY: Thirty isn't ancient.

JACK: Thirty-three. And, anyway, you haven't the slightest chance with him. Dan's a good guy, and he kids along with you, but that's just because he doesn't want to hurt you.

KATHY: I'm not complaining.

JACK: You mean you're satisfied to look at him sometimes and to exchange a few remarks.

KATHY: That's all I want. And all I expect.

JACK (*Stops his pacing and stands before divan, looking thoughtfully at* KATHY): Just like Elaine.

KATHY: And she was, in your own words, dizzy.

JACK: Please, Kathy. I don't think you're dizzy. I happen to think you're wonderful.

KATHY (*Softening*): And really, I think you're nice, too, Jack. I'm sorry about everything. Maybe I'm just mixed up. (*The doorbell rings.*)

JACK: Want me to answer it? (KATHY *nods.* JACK *goes to door and opens it.* SUE REYNOLDS, *an attractive girl in her middle twenties, and* DAN HOWARD, *a handsome man in his thirties, enter and come to center.*)

SUE: Hi, Sis. Hi, Jack. We're drenched. Let me take your coat, Dan. I'll hang it in the kitchen to dry.

DAN (*Removing coat*): Thanks, Sue. (SUE *exits left with coat.*)

JACK: Some weather, hey?

DAN: It's wet all right, but I don't really mind. Somehow

or other, I like the rain on my face. It makes me feel more alive.

KATHY: What a beautiful thought!

DAN (*Bowing*): Thank you, Kathy.

JACK: Well, the stuff just makes me feel wet and clammy.

KATHY: That's because you're not romantic like Dan.

JACK: I can be romantic (*Pointedly*) in the right time and place.

DAN: I'm sure you can, Jack. (*To* KATHY) And what have you been doing with yourself all day?

KATHY: Just sitting and reading.

DAN: Well, Sue and I have been a bit more active than that. (SUE *enters at left.*)

SUE: What's that about being active?

DAN: I was telling Kathy and Jack that we've certainly been on the go today.

SUE: I'll say we have. (*She sinks wearily into chair.*) First, we drove over to Benton to see Marge and Bill, and then we came back and did some shopping.

DAN (*Groaning*): And these bones are feeling their age.

KATHY (*Looking at him admiringly*): You'll never be old, Dan, because you're so young at heart.

JACK: Oh, brother!

DAN: That sounds like the title of a popular song, Kathy. "Young at Heart."

KATHY: Well, it fits you. (MRS. REYNOLDS *enters at left.*)

MRS. REYNOLDS: Kathy, would you help me out here for a few moments?

KATHY (*Rising*): Of course, Mother.

MRS. REYNOLDS: I'll try not to keep her for long, Jack. (KATHY *and* MRS. REYNOLDS *exit at left.* JACK *rises and goes to chair before fireplace, where he sits dejectedly.* SUE *and* DAN *sit on couch. There is silence.* SUE *looks at* DAN *and then nods pointedly in direction of* JACK. *She shrugs her shoulders.*)

DAN: You don't look like the happiest man on earth, Jack.

JACK (*Desolately*): I'm not.

SUE: What's wrong? We're great on settling other people's problems.

JACK: It's Kathy. She won't go to the dance with me to-night. Says she'd rather go to the movies with you.

SUE: Golly, that doesn't sound normal. When I was her age, I'd have given a month's supply of chocolate sundaes to go to a dance.

JACK: Not Kathy. (*To* DAN) And I guess you know why, Dan.

SUE: You mean, of course, that Kathy has a crush on Dan.

JACK: It's a crush all right.

SUE (*To* DAN): You see, sir—your charms are fatal.

DAN: Well, I wish they weren't. Kathy's a sweet kid, and none of us wants to hurt her in any way.

SUE: Of course she's sweet. But there ought to be something we could do. (UNCLE DENNIS *enters from left.*)

UNCLE DENNIS: A rainy afternoon to you all. What's everybody looking so serious about?

SUE: It's Kathy.

UNCLE DENNIS: What's she been up to?

JACK: She's nuts about Dan, that's what.

UNCLE DENNIS: Ah, yes—so I've been told.

SUE: And something should be done about it.

DAN: The question is—what? We don't want to hurt her.

UNCLE DENNIS: Of course you don't.

JACK (*Rising and crossing to door left*): Well, thanks for your sympathy, anyway. I'm going to get my coat. I'll leave by the back door. I sure hope you can think of something.

UNCLE DENNIS: Don't despair, my boy.

SUE: And come back tonight. Kathy may change her mind about that dance.

JACK: Thanks, Sue. I will. But I don't believe in miracles. (JACK *exits left*.)

DAN: Poor kid.

UNCLE DENNIS: Say, Dan, didn't you tell me once that you did some acting during your college days.

SUE (*Laughing*): Indeed he did! Why Dan was a sort of Marlon Brando and Sir Laurence Olivier rolled into one.

DAN: Spare my blushes, girl.

UNCLE DENNIS: Then, by golly, I have an idea, and I think it might work. Point is, we'll have to let everyone but Kathy in on the scheme, because maybe all of us will have a bit of acting to do. Are you folks game to carry out what I propose?

SUE: Courage is our middle name.

UNCLE DENNIS: Then listen. Tonight when Dan comes to take you to the movies, you— (*His voice trails off as the curtains close.*)

* * * *

SCENE 2

TIME: *Early the same evening.*

SETTING: *Same as Scene 1.*

AT RISE: KATHY *is again sitting before the fireplace, reading a magazine.* MRS. REYNOLDS *and* SUE *are seated on couch.* UNCLE DENNIS *is reading the newspaper in chair left.*

KATHY: Shouldn't Dan be here by now? The feature goes on at seven, and it'll take us at least ten minutes to drive to the movies.

SUE: You're right; he should be here. I was a little worried about him when he left here this afternoon, though. He wasn't feeling very well.

MRS. REYNOLDS: Nothing serious, I hope.

SUE: I don't think so.

UNCLE DENNIS (*Looking up from paper*): Maybe just some of that virus that's around now. This damp weather gets a lot of people down.

SUE: The rain has let up some, anyway. (*Pointedly*) Looks as though it might clear up for the dance, Kathy.

KATHY: The dance holds no interest for me, thank you.

MRS. REYNOLDS: Isn't Jack coming by later tonight?

KATHY: I don't see why he should. He knows I'm going to the movies. (*The doorbell rings.*)

SUE: That must be Dan now. (*She goes to door, and opens it.*) Hi. (DAN *enters. He is limping slightly.*)

DAN: Hello, everybody.

SUE: Want to take off your coat, and sit a while, or shall we leave right away?

DAN (*Wearily*): I'd like to rest a few minutes if I could.

SUE: Of course. We still have enough time. (*She helps him remove his coat.*)

DAN: Ouch!

SUE: What's the matter?

DAN: My shoulder's bothering me again. Must be this wet weather. Thanks, Sue. (SUE *places the coat on table.* DAN *limps to couch and sinks down wearily.*)

KATHY: Is something wrong with your leg, Dan?

DAN: It's my rheumatism, I think. It usually kicks up at this time of year.

UNCLE DENNIS: I know just how you feel. But you've got to expect these things, boy, when you get along in years.

MRS. REYNOLDS: Why haven't you seen Dr. West about this, Dan? Perhaps you need a checkup.

DAN (*Laughing rather bitterly*): Oh, I've seen him all right. And do you know what he said? He called me a hypochondriac.

KATHY: A hypo—?

UNCLE DENNIS: Chondriac. That's someone who thinks he's sick when he really isn't.

KATHY: But why should Dr. West call you one of those? I think he's pretty fresh.

DAN: Well, you see I've been to him several times in the last month. Guess he's getting tired of me.

KATHY: Several times?

SUE: Why, Dan. You never told me.

DAN: He thought it might be my teeth. (*Grasps his front teeth with thumb and forefinger*) But this upper plate is still good.

KATHY (*Astounded*): Upper plate!

DAN: Oh, yes, I had all my upper front teeth out last year. Hasn't done much for my rheumatism, though.

SUE: It hasn't done much for your eating either, Dan. Do you remember this afternoon Marge gave us some of that chewy candy, and you got the stuff caught in your upper plate? I felt sorry for you.

UNCLE DENNIS (*Sadly*): First our hair begins to go—then our teeth. No one escapes.

DAN: And then, of course, there's my myositis.

MRS. REYNOLDS: And just what is that in plain English, Dan?

DAN: Dr. West says it's a sort of inflammation of the muscles. He says there's not too much he can do about it. (*He rises slowly and begins to limp around the room*) Says it's caused by bodily changes as we grow older. If I sit too long, though, my leg stiffens up.

SUE: Then perhaps we ought not to go to the movies, Dan. After all, I don't want to have to carry you out of the theater.

DAN: Well, if you and Kathy wouldn't be disappointed—

SUE: Of course not.

MRS. REYNOLDS: After all, your health is more important than Hollywood.

DAN: And that reminds me. Could I trouble you for a glass of water?

SUE: I'll get it for you. (*She exits left.*)

UNCLE DENNIS (*Rises and goes to window*): Good. The rain's stopped.

KATHY (*Suddenly interested*): It has?

UNCLE DENNIS: Yep. And looks as though it's going to be a nice night, after all. I see a couple of stars out there trying to peep through.

MRS. REYNOLDS: Perhaps the change in the weather will make you feel better, Dan.

DAN: I hope so. But I think I've inherited a weak constitution from my father. He was a semi-invalid for twenty years.

KATHY: Twenty years!

DAN: Yes. And they say that sort of thing runs in families. (SUE *enters, carrying a glass of water. She hands it to* DAN.)

DAN: Thanks. (*He takes a bottle of pills from his pocket, opens the bottle, takes two of the pills and puts them in his mouth. Then he drinks the water.*) There. I almost forgot. I have to take these blamed things every three hours.

UNCLE DENNIS: And what are they supposed to cure?

DAN: They're for my nerves. I haven't been sleeping well

for a long time. Dr. West says I'm too tense. (KATHY *is now looking at* DAN *very closely, as if unable to believe her eyes.*)

SUE: Well, if we're not going to the movies, what shall we do?

DAN: Dr. West says a short walk is good for my myositis. Walking is supposed to help the circulation. We'll have to go slow though. I have to watch my heart.

SUE: Then we'll just creep along, I promise you. I'll get my coat. (SUE *exits left.*)

DAN (*Returns to couch and sits*): I'd better just sit a while before we start out. This leg is really bad tonight. I'm sorry, Kathy, about the movies.

KATHY: Oh, that's all right.

DAN: Some other time, maybe.

KATHY: Yes, some other time. (UNCLE DENNIS *crosses in front of couch, and, unseen by* KATHY, *winks in a conspiratorial manner at* DAN.) I think I'll go upstairs and get the book I was reading.

MRS. REYNOLDS (*Rising*): And I promised Mrs. Hopkins I'd drop in for a few moments tonight. I'd better change my dress, though. Mrs. Hopkins always has an eagle eye for what anyone wears, so I'd better look my best. Good night, Dan.

DAN: Good night, Mrs. Reynolds. Forgive my not rising, but— (*He points to his leg.*)

MRS. REYNOLDS: I understand. And I hope you'll soon be feeling better. (*She exits left.*)

KATHY: Good night, Dan. Have a nice walk.

DAN: Good night, Kathy. (KATHY *exits left.*)

UNCLE DENNIS (*Comes to* DAN *and shakes his hand*): An excellent performance, Marlon Brando.

DAN: And I feel like the world's prize heel. But do you think it worked?

UNCLE DENNIS: Like a charm. (SUE *enters at left. She is now wearing a coat.*)

SUE: Well, Mr. Hypochondriac, are you ready?

UNCLE DENNIS: I've been congratulating him on his acting.

SUE: I think we've accomplished what we wanted to. (DAN *goes to table and puts on his coat.*)

DAN: But I hope Kathy isn't hurt.

SUE: She may be a little disillusioned, Dan. But at her age, there's always tomorrow. (SUE *and* DAN *go to center door.*)

SUE: Good night, Uncle Dennis.

UNCLE DENNIS: Good night, Sue. Good night, Dan. Have a nice walk. (SUE *and* DAN *exit.* UNCLE DENNIS *goes to fireplace and looks thoughtfully at fire.* KATHY *enters, book in hand, and goes to chair at fireplace and sits.*)

UNCLE DENNIS: Settling down for a night of reading?

KATHY: I suppose so.

UNCLE DENNIS: You don't sound very enthusiastic.

KATHY: Uncle Dennis, did you know that Dan had so many things the matter with him?

UNCLE DENNIS (*Placing hand on her shoulder and speaking slowly*): Kathy, always remember this. The sands of time flow slowly, but they flow steadily and inevitably. (*Goes toward door left*) Good night, child. (KATHY *stares thoughtfully at fire. Then she speaks, as if to herself.*)

KATHY: The sands of time flow slowly, but they flow steadily and inevitably. (*The doorbell rings.* KATHY *goes to center and opens door. Surprised*) Jack!

JACK (*Entering*): Hi. I sort of expected you'd be at the movies.

KATHY (*Going to couch, followed by* JACK): I decided not to.

JACK: How come?

KATHY: That's a long and soul-shattering story.

JACK: Anyway, now that I'm here, and you're here, let me

have one more try. How about that dance? (*They both sit on couch.*)

KATHY (*After a pause*): Jack, have you ever had rheumatism?

JACK: Rheumatism! For Pete's sake, no!

KATHY: And, Jack—do you have your own teeth?

JACK (*Pointing to his molars*): Well, whose do you think they are?

KATHY: And have you ever been afflicted with myositis?

JACK: Afflicted with what? Say, what is this?

KATHY: Don't interrupt, please. And is your father in good health?

JACK: He's in the pink.

KATHY: Did you ever have a limp?

JACK: A limp? Sure, I hurt my ankle once playing football.

KATHY: But you're all right, now.

JACK (*Rising*): Sure! Look! (*He does a brief jig.*)

KATHY: Wonderful. And do you take pills every three hours?

JACK: Do I look like a candidate for the old folks' home? What is all this, anyway? (KATHY *rises and takes* JACK'S *hand.*)

KATHY: Just this. I'm going to the dance with you. (*He hugs her.*)

JACK: Swell! I don't know what this is all about, but I repeat—swell!

KATHY: I'll go up and change my dress right now. (*She exits left.* JACK *scratches his head in bewilderment. He sits on couch again, and begins happily to whistle a popular tune.* UNCLE DENNIS *enters at left.*)

UNCLE DENNIS: You sound on top of the world, my boy.

JACK: I am! Kathy's going to the dance with me. I don't know why, but she's going. And I don't have rheumatism.

UNCLE DENNIS (*Beginning to laugh heartily*): It's the sands of time, my boy, the sands of time.

JACK (*Bewildered*): The sands of time? (*He shrugs his shoulders, and, so contagious is* UNCLE DENNIS' *laughter that he begins to laugh, too, as the curtains close.*)

THE END

Production Notes

The Sands of Time

Characters: 3 male; 3 female.

Playing Time: 25 minutes.

Costumes: Everyday dress. Jack, Sue and Dan wear coats when they enter.

Properties: Magazine and book for Kathy, newspaper for Uncle Dennis, bottle of pills for Dan, glass of water.

Setting: The Reynolds living room is comfortably and tastefully furnished. A large couch is at center. At the right wall, there is a fireplace flanked by two easy chairs. Another easy chair is at left. Upstage center is a door leading to the front porch. At right of the door is a table holding magazines and a telephone. A window is to the left of the door. A door leading to the other rooms in the house is in the left wall.

Lighting: No special effects.

Stop the Presses!

Characters

SPUD FOGARTY, *City Editor of the* Daily Blabber
BERYL BEAM, *an attractive girl reporter*
JACK RIGGS, *a brash and breezy reporter*
MAMIE POTTS, *the Society Editor*
HORACE SIMMS, *a serious and scholarly cub reporter*
PRINCE ALI KABABA, *the ruler of Peraque*
1ST COPY BOY
2ND COPY BOY

SCENE 1

TIME: *Late one morning.*
SETTING: *The City Room of the* Daily Blabber.
AT RISE: *There is general confusion in the room.* SPUD *is yelling into one of the two telephones on his desk.* 1ST COPY BOY *enters hurriedly, puts one piece of paper on* BERYL BEAM'S *desk at downstage left, and another on* JACK RIGGS' *desk, at downstage right.* 1ST COPY BOY *exits quickly and* 2ND COPY BOY *rushes in and stands before* SPUD'S *desk, on which the other phone begins ringing.* BERYL BEAM *and* JACK RIGGS *continue working.*

SPUD (*Very loudly, for he is used to speaking above the din in the City Room*): I don't care how you get it—but get it, or you'll be out of a job. This is a newspaper, not a charity enterprise. And, for Pete's sake, get some zip in your story. Most of your stuff is as flat as your head! (*He bangs down receiver and looks at* 2ND COPY BOY.) What do you want?

2ND COPY BOY: Mamie Potts wants you to look over this feature. (*Both phones are now ringing.*)

SPUD: More stuff about the cream of the city's society. Well, wait a minute. (1ST COPY BOY *rushes in, deposits papers on all desks and rushes out again.* SPUD *picks up phone again.*) Hello . . . What? (*Angrily*) Look, Madam, this is not an information bureau. How should I know how to get soup stains off a tablecloth? Try turpentine. (*He slams down receiver.*) Drink it!

BERYL: Ooh, what a nasty man! (*Other phone is still ringing.*)

SPUD (*Answering other phone*): Hello . . . Yes, you bet I've seen the front page. Listen, lunkhead, "valiant" is spelled with "ant" on the end—not "ent." Didn't you ever compete in spelling bees when you were a kid? You guys down there in the press room are great samples of American education. Buy yourselves a dictionary. And change that spelling—or heads will roll! (*To* 2ND COPY BOY) What are you standing there for?

2ND COPY BOY: It's Mamie Potts' feature, Mr. Fogarty. She wants you to look at it.

SPUD (*Grabbing feature*): Let's see the thing. (*Phone rings again.* SPUD *answers it.*) Hello . . . City Desk . . . Oh, it's you, Jenkins . . . Day off? . . . Now, isn't that just too peachy for words! Look, Jenkins, you be down here to work inside of fifteen minutes, or you won't have a job to get a day off from. Get it? (*Slams down receiver*)

JACK: Alas, poor Jenkins, I knew him well.

SPUD: Tell Mamie I'll let her know about this in a few minutes.

2ND COPY BOY: Yes, sir. (*He exits left hurriedly and collides with* 1ST COPY BOY *who has an arm full of newspapers. These drop to the floor. Both* COPY BOYS *pick them up and distribute them to each of the three desks, then exit hurriedly, as always.*)

SPUD (*Again answering phone and shouting more than ever*): Hello! What? . . . (*He suddenly softens and begins to speak quietly and very deferentially.*) Yes, Mr. Cronkite. Sure I know how important it is . . . You bet we're trying, Mr. Cronkite, but we haven't had any luck so far. (JACK *signals* BERYL *from his desk and winks broadly at her.*)

SPUD: Yes, Mr. Cronkite . . . No, Mr. Cronkite . . . Sure, we'll keep working on it . . . Yes, I know we don't want to be scooped by any other paper . . . Yes, I see your point . . . Certainly, Mr. Cronkite . . . I realize that, Mr. Cronkite . . . All right, Mr. Cronkite . . . Goodbye, Mr. Cronkite. (*He hangs up with a deep sigh.*)

JACK: I imagine that was Mr. Cronkite.

SPUD (*Sarcastically and loudly*): Ha! Ha! Boy, you kill me with your humor, Jack! You ought to be doing a three-a-day in vaudeville with that talent!

BERYL: You're right, Boss. Snappy songs and witty sayings by Jack Riggs, the clown-prince of comedy. Followed by bird calls and animal imitations.

JACK: Spare my blushes, Beryl. I know you're really crazy about me.

BERYL: You're living in a dream world, Mr. Riggs.

JACK: Trouble, hey, Spud? Is Harvey Q. Cronkite, the world's greatest publisher, still giving you the old needle about Prince Ali Kababa?

SPUD: He's giving me the needle all right. Boy, why I ever

wanted to be city editor of this rag, I'll never know. Life
in the Siberian salt mines must be easier. Mother should
have warned me there'd be days like this. (*Phone rings.*
SPUD *answers it.*) Hello . . . Oh no—not that! Look,
Horace, I told you 235 Weston St. not 235 Eastern. The
fire's at Weston . . . No, don't bother. Get back here.
I'll know next time not to send a boy out on a man's
job. (*Bangs receiver down*) I send that young lug, Horace
Simms to a fire, and he can't even find it.

BERYL: Poor kid.

SPUD: Poor kid, my eye. He gives me the creeps.

BERYL: I think he's cute. He's so shy and gentle and
scholarly. And he's got such corny, idealistic ideas about
journalism. Besides, he likes me. He asked me for a date
yesterday.

SPUD: Oh, boy, that's a good one. A date! He'll probably
take you to the Museum for a thrilling day of looking at
Ming vases and Egyptian mummies. He ought to be a
college professor, not a reporter. These over-educated
guys give me the willies.

BERYL: I'll run my own romances, Boss. I like him, and
that's that. Now just what is this story about Prince Ali
Kababa? Yesterday was my day off, so I'm not in the
know.

JACK: It's a sad tale, Beryl—not fit for delicate ears.

SPUD: It's sad all right. This Prince Ali Kababa rules the
Middle-Eastern kingdom of Peraque. You've heard of
Peraque—it's a rich oil country.

BERYL: The Prince sounds like the answer to a girl's dream.
Oil—mmm! Lots of nice, pretty money in oil.

SPUD: He's not the answer to a newspaperman's dream, I
can tell you. He's over here on a special mission. He may

grant oil concessions to this country—and again he may not. Another world power is after his oil, too.

BERYL: Sounds like one of those novels of international intrigue.

SPUD: Phooey on international intrigue! The Prince is a pain in the neck. We hear on the grapevine that he's just about made up his mind—only nobody can get in to *talk* to him. He keeps himself surrounded by a bunch of body-guards who would frighten Dracula.

JACK: And don't I know it!

SPUD: Every newspaper in town has sent reporters to inter-view him; they get about as far as the hotel lobby before they're thrown out on their ears. Cronkite, naturally, wants somebody from the paper here to get to the Prince. It would be a feather in the *Daily Blabber's* hat.

BERYL: Say, I'd like to have a go at getting to see the Prince. Maybe he has a weakness for womanly charm and grace.

SPUD: That's a laugh. The *Gazette* sent Honey Halliwell over to the Prince's place. You know Honey—she looks like a movie star, except she's better looking. She didn't get to first base.

JACK: And just to show you how hopeless it is, even I couldn't get to see him.

BERYL: Don't tell me that Jack Riggs, the all-American miracle, failed on an assignment.

JACK: I know it seems incredible, but I did.

BERYL: So now what happens? Why not send Mamie Potts over? She can talk her way through a concrete wall.

SPUD: You people are loaded with helpful suggestions, aren't you. (COPY BOYS *rush in, put papers on all desks, then rush out.*) Mamie is a pretty good Society Editor, but that's all.

JACK: She writes some brilliant items, though. And I now quote: "Mrs. Cornelius Murphy cut her finger badly while peeling potatoes on her back porch yesterday afternoon." There's a nice swing to her prose.

SPUD (*Phone rings*): Do me a big˙favor, will you, Jack— *shut up!*

JACK: You're the boss.

SPUD (*On phone*): Hello . . . City Desk . . . Oh, it's you, Mamie . . . No, I haven't had a chance to look at your feature yet . . . O.K. Come on in. I'll glance over it before you get here. (*He hangs up, then picks up* MAMIE'S *story, reads through it quickly, begins to slice at it with his pencil, muttering to himself all the while.* 1ST COPY BOY *enters quickly, whistling a tune. He is carrying mail, which he distributes hurriedly.*)

SPUD: Stop that whistling!

1ST COPY BOY: Yes, sir. (*He exits rapidly.* MAMIE POTTS *enters right.*)

JACK: Hello, Mamie. How goes the battle?

BERYL: Hi, Mamie.

MAMIE: Hello, everybody. (*She goes to* SPUD'S *desk.*) How's it read?

SPUD: Mamie, is it absolutely necessary for you to use three words where one will do? You're drunk with the sight of your own adjectives.

MAMIE: Now, Spud. I just wanted to get some real class into the story. After all, I'm describing one of the finest estates in the city.

SPUD (*Resignedly*): Oh, well, I give up. (*He hands her the story*) If you want to talk about "classic Doric pillars, sublimely chaste in their marble symmetry and reminding one, somehow, of the grandeur that was Greece," that's your business.

MAMIE: That's the spirit.

SPUD (*Yelling*): Copy Boy! (1ST COPY BOY *rushes in from left.*)

1ST COPY BOY: Yes, sir.

SPUD: Run out and get me a cup of coffee and a ham sandwich. And no mustard, or I'll boil you in oil.

1ST COPY BOY: Yes, sir. (*He rushes out left.*)

MAMIE: The story's all right, then?

SPUD (*Wearily*): Sure. It's grand. It's dandy. It'll get you a Pulitzer Prize.

MAMIE: Don't be so bitter, Spud. You'll be getting ulcers on your ulcers. (HORACE SIMMS *enters at left.*)

SPUD: Speaking of ulcers—look who's here. Well, Horace, welcome home. You did a swell job on that fire story. Just brilliant.

HORACE (*Sheepishly*): I'm really sorry about that, Mr. Fogarty. I guess I just misunderstood you.

MAMIE: Think nothing of it, sweetie-pie, we all love you just the same.

BERYL: You bet we do. (HORACE *looks at her affectionately. She returns the look.*)

HORACE (*Blissfully*): Thanks . . .

SPUD: Sure, we're just crazy about reporters that can't even find a fire when it's in front of their noses. You've got a great future, boy—only you'd better get yourself a seeing-eye dog.

HORACE: I'm genuinely sorry, sir. I know I've let you down. But I didn't mean to, I assure you. I take my duties seriously.

JACK: You tell him, kid.

HORACE: To me, the press is one of the great citadels of freedom. Ever since I was a boy, I have wanted to be a part of it—to share in the good newspaperman's search for the truth.

JACK: Oh, brother.

MAMIE: Now, isn't that sweet! You're wonderful, Horace.

HORACE: And I still think I can make good, Mr. Fogarty, if you'll only give me the chance. For example, I know you're worried about this Prince Ali Kababa affair.

SPUD: Worried, he says! Kid, I'm petrified. If we don't do something about that—and soon—we'll all be looking for jobs.

HORACE: I know it, sir—and I think we should all help each other in these difficulties. Consequently, I offer my services on the assignment.

BERYL: Hear! Hear!

SPUD: You *what?*

HORACE: I have a feeling that I can get in to see the Prince. In fact, I'm quite sure that I can.

JACK: Boy, I like you, but I think you're getting in over your head. The Prince's bodyguards will make mince meat of you. (*He shudders.*) One of them's about seven feet tall, and he must weigh all of three hundred pounds. You'd be a dead duck.

SPUD (*Phone rings, and he answers it*): Hello . . . What? . . . Herman's Diner . . . Yeah, I wanted a ham sandwich . . . No! I don't want mustard on it! I told the kid I didn't . . . (*Slams receiver down*) What a day! What a paper! What a life!

HORACE: Well, sir, I ask you as a personal favor to me to give me the assignment. (*Dramatically*) I'll get the story. The *Daily Blabber* is never scooped.

BERYL: Give the kid a chance, Boss.

MAMIE: Sure, he might just pull it off, somehow or other.

SPUD: Are you people out of your minds or something? This guy couldn't find a fire if his own shirt was aflame.

And you want me to send him down to that den of thugs. He'd be lucky to get by with his life.

HORACE (*Bravely*): I shall be very distressed, sir, if you don't let me try.

SPUD (*Very angrily*): Look, cloth-head! I don't care two cents' worth whether you're distressed or not. I told you a while ago that I should know better than to send a boy out on a man's job. Well, that still goes. Now get out of here, and don't bother me! Go read the funny papers, or cut out paper dolls! Do something! But don't ask to do something that you're entirely incapable of!

BERYL: You're a hard man, Boss!

MAMIE: And your bark is just as bad as your bite.

HORACE (*Very dejected*): I always thought that in newspaper work, you could get ahead if you were willing to work hard. I'm willing. I tell you, sir, I'm very distressed. I might even apply for a position on another paper.

SPUD: That would be the best thing in the world for our circulation!

HORACE: I'm serious, sir.

SPUD: And so am I! Look, kid, get out of here before I really lose my temper! And go to any newspaper in the city!

HORACE: But, sir—

SPUD: Get out! And don't bother to come back! (HORACE *walks slowly to exit left and pauses at door.*)

HORACE: I still think the press is one of the great foundations of democracy. But you disappoint me, sir, with your lack of foresight.

SPUD (*Rising menacingly at desk*): Get out! (HORACE *exits hurriedly.*)

BERYL: Poor kid!

MAMIE: He's such a serious and well-meaning young fellow. You shouldn't be so hard on him, Spud. (1ST COPY BOY *enters at left, carrying a paper container of coffee and a sandwich wrapped in wax paper.*)

1ST COPY BOY: Here you are, sir. (*He places container and sandwich on* SPUD'S *desk.* SPUD *hands him* MAMIE'S *story.*)

SPUD: Take this down to the pressroom.

1ST COPY BOY: Yes, sir. (*He exits left, hurriedly.*)

MAMIE: I'll be getting back to work.

SPUD (*Unwraps sandwich, takes a bite, and nearly gags*): There's mustard on it!

BERYL (*Choking with laughter*): That's a shame, Spud.

MAMIE (*Going toward exit left*): My heart bleeds for you. (*She exits. Phone rings.*)

SPUD (*Answering phone*): Hello . . . Yes, Mr. Cronkite . . . No, not yet. I'm still working on it . . . What? . . . Well, it's been a long time . . . Sure, if you say so, Mr. Cronkite. . . . Goodbye, Mr. Cronkite.

JACK: Mr. Cronkite, maybe?

SPUD: It was Cronkite all right! Guess what he wants me to do!

BERYL: Don't keep us in suspense, Boss.

SPUD: He wants me to go down to try to interview Prince Ali Kababa.

JACK: He does! (*Laughing*) Say, that's rich!

SPUD: You think it's a joke, huh. I suppose you think I've forgotten how to go out and get a story myself. Well, don't fool yourself! I can still do a good day's work!

JACK: Take my word for it, Spud. It's hopeless!

SPUD: Oh, is that so? Well, just because you and a few others couldn't bring in the story, don't think that a really good newspaperman can't deliver the goods! (*Rising and coming to center.*) By golly, this is a challenge! I'll show you people how a real reporter works! I've still got the touch!

BERYL: You'll be sorry!

SPUD: Don't kid yourself. Take over the desk, Jack! If anybody wants me, I'll be down chatting cosily with Prince Ali Kababa!

JACK: I admire your courage.

SPUD: It's not courage—it's just plain, honest-to-goodness know-how! You'll be able to see how a master works.

BERYL: That's what I like, Boss—modesty.

SPUD: I'll see you later—with the story! (*He exits left.*)

JACK: Stop the presses! Spud Fogarty rides again! (*The curtain closes.*)

CURTAIN

* * * *

SCENE 2

TIME: *About two hours later.*

SETTING: *Same as Scene 1.*

AT RISE: JACK *is sitting at* SPUD'S *desk.* BERYL *is working at her own desk.* MAMIE POTTS *is standing at center.*

MAMIE: I'll say one thing. Without Spud around here, this place is as peaceful as a Sunday afternoon in West Overshoe, Alaska.

BERYL: Even the phone doesn't ring so much. Spud is like a magnet. Confusion is attracted to him.

JACK: Wouldn't it be something if he really came back with the story!

MAMIE: Don't sell Spud short. He was a good reporter in his day. When I first joined the *Blabber* staff, Spud was the ace reporter. (1ST COPY BOY *rushes in left and begins to distribute papers.*)

JACK: Slow down, kid. The boss isn't here.

1ST COPY BOY: He isn't?

JACK: Nope.

1ST COPY BOY: Well, in that case. (*He slows down to a snail-like crawl as* 2ND COPY BOY *rushes in.*) Put on the brakes, Joe. Gravel voice is among the missing.

2ND COPY BOY: Oh, boy! (*He, too, slows down to a snail's pace. When papers are distributed, both boys amble out slowly.*)

JACK: I wonder if one of the other papers has grabbed our friend Horace. Golly, Spud really pinned his ears back!

MAMIE: You know that Horace appeals to me. If I were twenty years younger, I could go for him. It must be my maternal instinct.

BERYL: He's cute, all right.

JACK: With a handsome fellow like me around, I don't see how you girls have eyes for anyone else.

BERYL: You know, Jack, the romance between you and yourself is one of the great love affairs of our time.

MAMIE: But if Spud does return with that Prince Ali Kababa story, your ego will be deflated—and plenty.

BERYL: You can say that again, Mamie. In fact, life around here will be pretty hectic. Spud will be lording it over all of us like Louis XIV over his court. (*Phone rings.* JACK *answers it.*)

JACK: City desk . . . No, he's not here . . . Oh, hello, Mr. Cronkite . . . Yes, he left about two hours ago to get the story . . . I'll be glad to, Mr. Cronkite . . . Yes, I'll have him call you as soon as he returns . . . Sure thing, Mr. Cronkite . . . Goodbye, Mr. Cronkite.

MAMIE: So the big boy is checking up again?

JACK: He sure is. Heaven help all of us if Spud doesn't return loaded with honors!

MAMIE: I've been around here long enough to know that when Cronkite gets an idea in his head, he sticks with it to the bitter end. He can't stand failure in anybody, and he can be tough, let me tell you.

BERYL: You're making us feel too cheerful for words. (1ST COPY BOY *and* 2ND COPY BOY *enter left excitedly.*)

1ST COPY BOY: The boss is on his way up!

2ND COPY BOY: He just got out of a taxi downstairs. I saw him through the window.

JACK: How's he look?

2ND COPY BOY: I don't know. I rushed right in here with the glad tidings.

MAMIE: Well, we'd better look busy. (*She picks up a paper from* BERYL'S *desk and begins reading it intently.* JACK *begins using his editor's pencil on a story.* BERYL *starts to type frantically.*)

1ST COPY BOY: We'd better clear out, Joe, or he might find something for us to do.

2ND COPY BOY: Roger! (*They exit hurriedly left. A moment or two passes, and then* SPUD *enters slowly at left. His left arm is in a sling, there is a piece of adhesive on his forehead, and he is limping.*)

JACK: Hail the conquering hero!

MAMIE: What happened to you, Spud? You look as though you'd been caught in a meat grinder. (SPUD *goes to city desk.*)

SPUD: Get up, Jack. Let me sit there before I fall down. (JACK *rises quickly and returns to his own desk.* SPUD *sits down with a groan.*)

BERYL: Did you get to the Prince's hotel, Spud?

SPUD (*Weakly*): Oh, yes, I got there all right. That was easy.

MAMIE: And what about Prince Ali Kababa? Did you get to see him?

SPUD (*Grimacing*): Do me a favor, Mamie. Don't even mention his name. I might as well tell you the story. I got to the hotel and into the lobby. I asked at the desk for the number of the Prince's suite. I said I was a masseur called in by the Prince.

BERYL: That was brilliant, Boss.

SPUD: Yeah, I'm a genius. So I got on the elevator and rode up to Room 872. Outside the room, there were a couple of guys with beards and turbans; they were built along the lines of those wrestlers you see on television. I told them I was a masseur and that the Prince was expecting me. Each of the turbaned guys grabbed me under the arms, bounced me a couple of times on the floor, and dragged me back to the elevator. One of the guys put such pressure on my arm that I've got a bad sprain. Had to see Doc Benson about it, and he fixed up this sling. One of the guys rang for the elevator. When it came, they threw me in. I banged my head (*He touches the adhesive gingerly*) against the wall. And here I am.

BERYL: Tough luck, Boss.

JACK: That reminds me, Spud, Cronkite wants you to call him.

SPUD: Oh, that's wonderful! That'll just be the climax to a perfect day!

JACK: Well, I don't like to say I told you so—but I told you so.

BERYL: Don't rub it in, Jack.

MAMIE: No, let's try to be humanitarian about all this.

SPUD: One thing I know—if I couldn't get the story, nobody can.

MAMIE: Now you sound more like yourself, Spud.

JACK: What are you going to tell Cronkite?

SPUD (*Holding his head*): Please! Don't remind me of Cronkite! He'll be wild! (1ST COPY BOY *rushes in at left, catches sight of* SPUD'S *condition, and hastily stifles whoop of laughter.*) Something strike you as funny, kid?

1ST COPY BOY: No, sir.

SPUD: Then control yourself. What do you want in here, anyway?

1ST COPY BOY: It's about Horace, sir.

SPUD: Horace! You mean that lunkhead, Horace Simms! Well, what about him?

1ST COPY BOY: He just came into the building with a very queer looking guy. They're on their way up.

SPUD: All right—you've carried your message to Garcia. Now get out!

1ST COPY BOY: Yes, sir. (*He exits left, hurriedly.*)

SPUD (*Sarcastically*): So Horace is back with us. I guess the other rags in town didn't jump at the chance to acquire his services.

MAMIE: Be nice to him, Spud. He's probably upset.

SPUD: Upset! That's a good one! And what do you think I am after my experience? Upset is a mild word! (HORACE *enters at left. He is smiling and looks confident. Following him is a slim, dark-haired young man who is wearing a turban and very natty clothes.*)

HORACE (*Coming to* SPUD): Well, Mr. Fogarty, here I am!

SPUD: Isn't that just wonderful. (*Pointing at him*) Look, I told you to go—go to the *Clarion*, go to the *Bugle*, go to blazes for all of me, but go— (*He stops suddenly and realizes that he is now pointing at the turbaned stranger. All at once, he realizes this is* PRINCE ALI KABABA. *He smiles weakly.*) Just kidding, Horace.

HORACE (*Dramatically*): I should like to introduce you to his royal highness, Prince Ali Kababa of Peraque.

MAMIE: Golly, the kid did it!

JACK: Holy smoke!

BERYL: Gosh, Prince Ali Kababa!

HORACE (*To* PRINCE): Senaken juraki beletam.

PRINCE (*Smiling*): Dowakin galama suritani bedgardisun. (SPUD, MAMIE, JACK, *and* BERYL *are bewildered.*)

HORACE: Please forgive my speaking in a foreign tongue, but I wanted the Prince to know his story will appear in an extra edition of the *Blabber*.

SPUD: What's that language you're spouting?

HORACE: Peraquian.

SPUD: Peraquian! You speak Peraquian?

HORACE: At college, I was interested in Middle Eastern tongues. Peraquian is a language I devoted considerable time to.

JACK: Kid, you're amazing!

BERYL: Horace, you're just plain wonderful!

SPUD: You mean to say you got in to see the Prince?

HORACE: It was not difficult at all. I spoke Peraquian to his guards, and they were delighted. It seems they haven't been able to find anybody around here who can speak their language. The Prince was happy to see me. We had a long talk, and I invited him over here for a tour of the newspaper plant. He is very interested in American newspapers.

PRINCE (*Holding up his hand imperiously for silence*): Please— my English, it is not so good, but I like to deliver a few words.

SPUD (*Softening and very polite*): Go right ahead, Prince. It's an honor to have you here.

PRINCE: I have granted the oil—now, how do you say it—

HORACE (*Beaming*): Concessions?

PRINCE: Ah, yes, thank you, friend Horace—I have granted the oil concessions to your so beautiful country. It is your great newspaper that shall have the—how do you call it—?

HORACE: Privilege?

PRINCE: Yes, that is it. Thank you, friend Horace. It is your great newspaper that shall have the privilege of telling this to the world.

SPUD (*Rises and comes quickly to center where he shakes the PRINCE's hand*): Prince, you're a prince.

MAMIE: Of course he's a prince.

BERYL: And, if you ask me, Spud, you ought to give Horace a raise.

SPUD (*Agreeably*): Sure thing!

HORACE (*Rather uncomfortably*): I'm afraid that won't be necessary, sir.

JACK: Don't be silly, kid. You deserve it.

HORACE: Thank you, but I'm afraid I will not be on the *Daily Blabber's* staff—at least not for a while.

SPUD: Oh, look now, kid, I hope you're not sore about anything I said to you. After all, we all lose our tempers once in a while.

HORACE: No, sir, I'm not angry at all. But the Prince has made me an excellent offer. I am returning to Peraque with him to take charge of his newspaper for a year. He was very impressed by what I told him about American journalism. I assured him that the backbone of any nation is the press—a free press that searches out the truth and disseminates it for all to read. (*Proudly*) I am going to reform the Peraquian press. It is just the sort of challenge

I have always dreamed of. But after a year, I shall, of course, return to America. After all, for an American, this is the only country. The Prince understands.

BERYL: Say, you don't need a girl Friday, do you?

HORACE (*To* PRINCE): Gwazadem eni kabalaza gimi? Ud pazetem mulera quandimiza.

PRINCE (*Goes to* BERYL *and looks at her carefully. Then he nods his head and smiles*): Preaznami progatem! Ud mulera quandimiza gretanasa!

BERYL: What's he saying?

HORACE: He thinks you're a pretty girl and that you look very intelligent. He thinks you'll make an excellent secretary for me.

BERYL: Well, thanks, Your Highness.

PRINCE: You are welcome.

SPUD: Now wait a minute! What are you trying to do—take my whole staff away from me?

BERYL: Peraque calls, boss. So does Horace. (*She smiles at* HORACE *affectionately*.) And I'm going. But don't be bitter; it's only for a year.

JACK: You mean you'll leave me—the light of your life?

BERYL: You'll just have to take it like the great big man you are, Jack. I'm leaving, and that's that.

JACK: It's a blow to my pride, you know.

MAMIE (*To* JACK): I imagine you'll survive.

HORACE: And now I shall take the Prince on a tour of our plant. He is most anxious to see the pressroom in operation.

PRINCE: I wish to thank all of you for your—now how do you say it—

HORACE: Courtesy?

PRINCE: Courtesy, yes. Thank you, friend Horace. For your courtesy. Lamani gazada.

HORACE: He says goodbye.

MAMIE (*Dropping a curtsey*): Goodbye, Prince.

JACK: So long, Your Highness.

BERYL: Au revoir, but not goodbye. See you in Peraque.

SPUD (*Weakly*): Lamani gazada.

PRINCE (*Smiling happily*): Lamani gazada. (*He and* HORACE *exit left.*)

JACK: Now I've seen everything.

MAMIE: I knew that Horace had the stuff in him. But cheer up, Spud. He'll be back in a year. And we can certainly use that boy around here. (SPUD *returns to his desk and sits down.*)

BERYL: And we've got the story. (*Dramatically*) The *Daily Blabber* is never scooped! Isn't Horace great? (*The phone rings.* SPUD *picks up receiver.*)

SPUD: Hello. Oh, yes, Mr. Cronkite.

HORACE (*Appearing suddenly in left doorway*): Beryl, the Prince would like you to tour the plant with us—and so would I.

BERYL: Nothing I'd like better than to be with you.

JACK: Ha! (BERYL *exits quickly left.*)

SPUD: That's right, Mr. Cronkite. We got the story—exclusive . . . Er- er- well, no, I didn't exactly get it myself. But I sent out one of my bright young men with complete instructions as to how to go about it.

JACK: Oh, brother!

SPUD: Yes, that's right. Horace Simms is his name. Very bright young fellow. Speaks Peraquian . . . What's that? . . . Give him a promotion? Well, er- er- well, the fact is he won't be with us again for a year . . . He— Yes, Mr. Cronkite . . . Yes, I know that . . . Yes, I'm sorry, but he is coming back . . . Well, no, Mr. Cronkite . . . Well, I'm sorry you feel that way . . . I did everything

I could to keep him, but he *is* coming back in a year. But . . .

JACK: Stop the presses! Cronkite is on the warpath again! (SPUD *is still sputtering unhappily into the phone as the curtain closes.*)

THE END

Production Notes

STOP THE PRESSES!

Characters: 6 male; 2 female.

Playing Time: 30 minutes.

Costumes: Spud Fogarty works in his shirt sleeves, his tie loosened and his sleeves rolled up; the jacket of his business suit is draped over his chair and he puts on the jacket when he leaves on assignment. Beryl Beam wears an attractive suit and high-heeled shoes. Mamie Potts wears a suit also, dowdier than Beryl's. Jack Riggs wears a loud vest and flashy necktie under his suit. Horace Simms wears a charcoal gray suit and white buckskin shoes. Prince Ali Kababa wears a turban of rich-looking cloth, and possibly a tuxedo or navy blue suit. The copy boys wear slacks, shirts with rolled-up sleeves; one of them might wear a sleeveless sweater.

Properties: Two telephones, three typewriters, sheets of copy, scratch paper, miscellaneous pencils, papers, paper clips, etc., several newspapers, sandwich wrapped in wax paper, sling, Band-aids.

Setting: The City Room of the *Daily Blabber*. Spud Fogarty's desk stands at center of stage. On this desk are a typewriter and two telephones. Beryl Beam's desk is at downstage left; there is a typewriter on it. At downstage right stands Jack Riggs' desk, which also holds a typewriter. There are miscellaneous papers, pencils, etc. strewn over all three desks and also on the floor. On the upstage wall

79

is a calendar, with printed slogans pinned up on either side: "GET THAT STORY" and "*THE DAILY BLABBER* IS NEVER SCOOPED." There are exits at left and right.

Lighting: No special effects.

The Case of the Missing Pearls

Characters

BUXTON ANGUISH, *a wealthy, retired British diplomat*
PENELOPE ANGUISH, *his wife*
MRS. SLIPCOVER, *their housekeeper*
HERMIONE ANGUISH, *an attractive, delicate girl of eighteen*
MONTY DARE, *her fiancé, a breezy young fellow of twenty*
ALICE PADDLECART, *Hermione's friend, about Hermione's age*
SLIPCOVER, *the butler*
SHELLACK HOMES, *the great detective*
DR. JON WHOOPSON, *his faithful companion*
HANDSOME HOGAN, *a brilliant member of Scotland Yard*

SCENE 1

SETTING: *The living room of the country estate of* BUXTON ANGUISH.

AT RISE: BUXTON ANGUISH *is seated in easy chair downstage right. His wife,* PENELOPE ANGUISH, *is seated left of table.* MRS. SLIPCOVER, *the housekeeper, is standing beside* MRS. ANGUISH.

MRS. SLIPCOVER: And how many will there be for lunch, Mrs. Anguish?

81

MRS. ANGUISH (*Sighing*): More than we originally expected, Mrs. Slipcover. Let me see now. There will, of course, be Mr. Anguish and myself. You are going to have lunch, are you not, Buxton?

MR. ANGUISH: Indeed, I am, Penelope, my dear.

MRS. ANGUISH: Then there will be Hermione and Monty Dare—

MRS. SLIPCOVER: Oh, and don't they make a lovely couple!

MRS. ANGUISH: And Miss Paddlecart—

MRS. SLIPCOVER: Isn't she going home soon?

MR. ANGUISH: Why, Mrs. Slipcover, you're not anxious to get rid of Miss Paddlecart, are you? She's a charming young woman and an old school friend of Hermione's.

MRS. SLIPCOVER: Oh, no, sir. I'm not trying to get rid of her.

MRS. ANGUISH: And then, of course, since they'll be arriving before lunch time, I expect, there'll be Mr. Shellack Homes and his friend, Dr. Jon Whoopson.

MRS. SLIPCOVER: Oh, ma'am, I can hardly wait to get a look at him. Just think of having a great detective like Mr. Shellack Homes right in the same house. Slipcover and I spent half the night talking about it.

MR. ANGUISH: Er—Mrs. Slipcover, did your husband walk in his sleep again last night?

MRS. SLIPCOVER: No, sir. After Slipcover retired about eleven, and after our chat about Mr. Shellack Homes, he never stirred a muscle.

MR. ANGUISH: Good. I've been worried about him. Sleepwalking butlers aren't exactly my particular cup of tea.

MRS. ANGUISH: And especially since there have been so many weird happenings here for the past two weeks. In any event, Mrs. Slipcover, there'll be seven for lunch, as far as I can tell.

MRS. SLIPCOVER: Very good, ma'am. Will a bit of con-
sommé, a nice piece of sole, and a gooseberry tart be all
right?

MR. ANGUISH: Splendid, Mrs. Slipcover. I'm very fond of
gooseberry tart.

MRS. SLIPCOVER: Very good, sir. I'll be about my business
then. (*She exits*)

MRS. ANGUISH: Oh, Buxton, do you really think Mr. Homes
will be able to solve the mystery of my missing pearls?

MR. ANGUISH: If he can't, my dear, I don't know who can.
The man has a trigger mind and an uncanny intuition.

MRS. ANGUISH: The pearls meant so much to me. You
remember, Buxton, you gave them to me on my fourth
anniversary.

MR. ANGUISH: Of course, my dear.

MRS. ANGUISH: And I've always been so careful of them.
In fact, when I'm not wearing them, I unstring them
and hide each one in a different place. And yet, last week,
one of them was stolen from the drawer of the desk in
our room.

MR. ANGUISH: And this week, one was taken from the
medicine cabinet.

MRS. ANGUISH: And the night before last we heard those
horrible cries in the night. They seemed to come from
outside somewhere.

MR. ANGUISH: Not to forget the mysterious fire in the south
barn last week.

MRS. ANGUISH: Oh, Buxton, what does it all mean? There
is something evil loose around us. I am frightened, Buxton, frightened. (MR. ANGUISH *rises and comes over to his
wife and pats her hand.*)

MR. ANGUISH: There, there, my dear, be of good cheer.
Shellack Homes will soon be here, and I feel certain he

will be able to throw light on the dark doings that have so terrified you.

MRS. ANGUISH: Oh, Buxton, I hope you are right and that your confidence in Mr. Homes will be justified.

MR. ANGUISH: It will, my dear, never fear. (HERMIONE ANGUISH *and* MONTY DARE *enter hand in hand, from upstage center door.*)

HERMIONE: Hello, Mother. Hello, Father. We have had the loveliest walk. The spring air is like wine today, and all the flowers are beginning to bud.

MONTY: Yet nothing that spring has to offer is so lovely as your fair daughter, Mr. and Mrs. Anguish.

HERMIONE: Oh, Monty.

MONTY: It's true, Hermione. You're the fairest flower of the season.

HERMIONE: I am so excited today at the prospect of seeing the great Shellack Homes in person.

MONTY: I want you to know, Mrs. Anguish, how deeply sorry I am about the loss of your pearls. It was a dastardly deed. (*Drawing himself up*) And I promise to do all in my poor power to expose the perpetrator of so foul a crime.

HERMIONE: Oh, Monty! How wonderful you are!

MR. ANGUISH: Thank you, my boy, for those kind sentiments. My wife and I are most grateful.

HERMIONE: When I was awakened last night by those dreadful, inhuman cries, I trembled like a small child in the midst of a horrible nightmare. Oh, what can be happening to our once so happy home? What monstrous creature is afoot? (ALICE PADDLECART, *a pretty girl of* HERMIONE'S *age, enters.*)

ALICE: Hermione, darling, you seem upset. What is it? (*She comes to* HERMIONE *and takes both her hands.*)

HERMIONE: It's the dreadful happenings of the past two weeks that have upset me, Alice.

ALICE: All will be well. Do you remember how at school you sometimes became frightened by little things?

HERMIONE: And you always comforted me, Alice.

ALICE: And so I shall now. Don't worry. The great Mr. Homes will soon be here. (SLIPCOVER, *the butler, a thin, solemn-looking man, enters.*)

MR. ANGUISH: Yes, Slipcover.

SLIPCOVER: Mr. Shellack Homes and Dr. Jon Whoopson.

MR. ANGUISH: Show them in at once, Slipcover.

SLIPCOVER: Very good, sir. (*He exits left.*)

MONTY: At last—the great Shellack Homes!

MRS. ANGUISH: This is the moment we all have been waiting for. (SLIPCOVER *returns, followed by* SHELLACK HOMES *and* DR. JON WHOOPSON. HOMES *is carrying a violin case under his arm.* DR. WHOOPSON *is a hearty man in his thirties.*)

SLIPCOVER: Mr. Shellack Homes. Dr. Jon Whoopson.

MR. ANGUISH (*Coming forward and holding out his hand to* HOMES): This is a great pleasure, Mr. Homes. I am Buxton Anguish. And how do you do, Dr. Whoopson.

DR. WHOOPSON: Very well, thank you. (HOMES *lays his violin case on divan, takes a magnifying glass from his pocket, and on all fours, he begins to scrutinize the floor.*)

ALICE: Oh, how wonderful! Mr. Homes wastes no time.

DR. WHOOPSON: Please, miss. We must have silence. Homes is concentrating—as only he can. (*All stare, fascinated, as* HOMES, *on hands and knees, does his detecting.* MRS. SLIPCOVER *enters and also stares intently.*)

MRS. SLIPCOVER: What a wonderful sight!

SLIPCOVER: Shh, Henrietta. Mr. Homes is concentrating.

MONTY: As only he can.

HOMES (*Now at a spot near bookcase*): Aha!

DR. WHOOPSON: Found something, my dear fellow?

HOMES: Possibly, Whoopson. Possibly. (*He rises, with something that looks like dust in his hand, and intently examines the material through his magnifying glass.*) Ah, yes. I recognize the ash, of course. It somewhat resembles latakia, and yet there are differences. Someone in this house has been smoking Italian cheroots. I have, as you perhaps know, written a monograph on the characteristics of tobacco ash. (*He goes to* MRS. SLIPCOVER) Will you hold out your right hand, please? (*She does so, rather hesitantly.*) Ah, yes, the nicotine stain between thumb and forefinger. You, madam, are the cheroot smoker. (*All are amazed at this revelation.*)

MRS. ANGUISH: Why, Mrs. Slipcover, I never knew you used tobacco!

MRS. SLIPCOVER (*Sheepishly*): Well, ma'am, I've been trying to break myself of the filthy habit. I first became addicted to Italian cheroots when I was in the service of the Countess Ravioli in Italy. She always smoked one before bedtime and insisted each night that I join her.

HOMES (*Looking fixedly at* MR. ANGUISH): I note, sir, that you have spent some time in India.

MR. ANGUISH: Good heavens! You're uncanny, Mr. Homes. How could you possibly have guessed? I was in the diplomatic service there for twenty-five years.

HOMES: Elementary, my dear Anguish. I note that your bookcase is filled with tomes concerning India. I note, too, that on the wall of your reception room, where I came in, there is a print by the Hindu artist, Gowmorrarah Suwiladi. According to the inscription on the print, he presented it to you.

MRS. ANGUISH: Remarkable.

HERMIONE: How thrilling!

MONTY: You have keen perception, sir.

HOMES: None keener. But now, let us to the business that has brought me here. This circumstance of the missing pearls must be most distressing to you, Mrs. Anguish. I know, of course, about their sentimental value—an anniversary present, were they not?

MRS. ANGUISH: Yes.

HOMES: It would appear from what you have told me that some member of the household must be the guilty one.

MR. ANGUISH: Oh, my dear Homes, I think not. The servants have been with us for years. And our house guests are above reproach.

HOMES: I should appreciate being introduced to your house guests.

MR. ANGUISH: Of course. This is Alice Paddlecart, an old school friend of my daughter, Hermione.

HOMES (*Bowing*): A pleasure, Miss Paddlecart. I observe you are a great lover of flowers and that you are partial to lemonade.

ALICE (*Astounded*): How in the world did you know?

DR. WHOOPSON (*Chuckling*): There's not much he doesn't know, I can tell you.

HOMES: Elementary, my dear Miss Paddlecart. Really elementary. There is a bit of lemon peel on your lower lip. (ALICE *wipes mouth.*) And on your hands there is the telltale stain that is made only, from my observation, by the type of rose that is known as the Supreme—*roseatis suprematis*, to give it its Latin term.

MRS. SLIPCOVER: He's a genius, that's what he is.

MR. ANGUISH: And this is Monty Dare, my daughter Hermione's fiancé.

MONTY (*Breezily*): And what can you tell about me, Mr. Homes?

HOMES: You ride a bicycle, you have recently taken a trip by train, and your sciatica is improving.

MONTY (*Completely astonished*): But how—

HOMES: Too simple, really, my dear Dare, to merit detailed explanation. However, there is a sort of ring around your trouser cuffs—a ring obviously made by bicycle clips. The stub of a railway ticket protrudes from your upper pocket. And you walk with a slight limp, occasionally pressing your hand to your right hip, a sure sign that you have fairly recently been plagued either by sciatica or lumbago.

HERMIONE: It's all so easy when you explain it, Mr. Homes.

DR. WHOOPSON: Exactly. But none of us has trained himself to observe so minutely as my friend Homes.

HOMES: Mr. Dare and Miss Paddlecart are your only house guests at present, Mr. Anguish.

MR. ANGUISH: Yes. They have been here for several weeks.

HOMES (*Thoughtfully*): Indeed. And how long have Mr. and Mrs. Slipcover been in your service?

MRS. SLIPCOVER: Ten years, sir, come Michaelmas.

MRS. ANGUISH: They are good and faithful servants.

MR. ANGUISH: And yet, of late, Slipcover has been walking in his sleep.

HOMES (*Interested*): Aha! Has he? (*He takes long and purposeful strides toward* SLIPCOVER, *and, with his magnifying glass, looks into* SLIPCOVER's *eyes.*) Ah, most interesting. A slight dilation of the iris, although the retina appears almost normal. Tell me, my good man, is sleepwalking common with you? Or is it a recent development?

SLIPCOVER: Most recent, Mr. Homes. Until last week, I never sleepwalked in my life.

HOMES: Hmm, interesting. Most interesting. As the French say, it makes one furiously to think. (*To* MRS. ANGUISH) And now, madam, what of the mysterious cries that have been heard in the night?

HERMIONE: Oh, Mr. Homes, they were inhuman—like an animal in distress.

HOMES: Indeed. And what of the south barn—it was burned last week, was it not?

MR. ANGUISH: To a cinder.

HOMES: You believe that someone set the fire?

MR. ANGUISH: I think it highly possible, Mr. Homes.

HOMES: Most interesting. You note, Whoopson, my dear fellow, how the plot thickens. The game is afoot, and we must keep our wits about us.

DR. WHOOPSON: You're right, my dear Homes.

HOMES: I think, Mr. and Mrs. Anguish, that I can promise you a solution to the strange happenings within twenty-four hours.

MRS. SLIPCOVER: He's a living miracle, that's what he is!

HOMES: Thank you, madam. You are most kind—and most correct.

MONTY: I hope, Mr. Homes, that you succeed. Dear Hermione has become a bundle of nerves since these dreadful things began to happen.

ALICE (*Slipping her arm about* HERMIONE's *waist*): Hermione has always been delicate and fragile.

MONTY (*Laying his hand on* ALICE's *shoulder*): But you and I, Alice, will do all we can to protect her from further terrors.

HOMES: Indeed? Most interesting. (*He goes to divan where he picks up his violin case.*) And now, with your permission, I shall confine myself to a few moments on my violin. I find that music helps me to concentrate.

MR. ANGUISH: Please feel at liberty to do whatever you wish, Mr. Homes.

HOMES: Thank you, my dear fellow. (*He removes violin from case, tucks violin under his chin, takes bow, and begins to play. The result is a horrible concoction of weird and cacophonous playing. The others grimace as the music grows worse and worse. Only* DR. WHOOPSON *looks on with genuine admiration.*)

DR. WHOOPSON: Capital, my dear Homes, capital. I recognize your favorite tune, Clementi's "Night in a Turkish Bath." (*The others continue to grimace and shudder.* WHOOPSON *looks entranced, and* HOMES *continues to saw away as the curtain falls.*)

* * * *

SCENE 2

SETTING: *The same, at midnight.*

AT RISE: HOMES *and* DR. WHOOPSON *are the only occupants of the room.* HOMES *is lying on the divan, hands locked behind his head, the picture of solid comfort.* DR. WHOOPSON, *who appears somewhat nervous, is pacing the floor.*

HOMES: My dear Whoopson, there really is no need for your eternal pacing up and down. Serenity, my dear fellow, is what is needed.

DR. WHOOPSON: I can't help feeling, my dear Homes, that something of terrible consequence may happen here tonight.

HOMES: Exactly. That is why you and I are passing the midnight hours in this room when everyone in the household thinks we are snugly in bed. Does this not remind you, my dear Whoopson, of our midnight vigil when we were pursuing the case of the speckled canary?

DR. WHOOPSON (*Shuddering*): It does, indeed. I was nearly killed that night. On damp days, the knee through which the bullets passed still gives me difficulty.

HOMES: Hazards of our occupation, my dear Whoopson, hazards of our occupation. (*Sits up suddenly*) But, quiet, I hear footsteps. A man's, I believe. (SLIPCOVER, *the butler, enters right. His eyes are partially closed, and he walks with his hands stretched before him. He is obviously walking in his sleep.*) (*Softly*) Aha! Our old friend, Slipcover. I suspected he might appear on the scene.

DR. WHOOPSON: Is he the culprit?

HOMES: Not at all, Whoopson. He is a man more sinned against than sinning. (SLIPCOVER *walks around the room slowly.* HOMES *rises, goes to* SLIPCOVER, *and takes him by the shoulders.*)

HOMES: Note now, Whoopson, the great benefits I have derived from my study of hypnotism with the late and great Professor Longdoze.

DR. WHOOPSON: You mean that Slipcover is a victim of hypnosis?

HOMES: Indubitably. When I examined his eyes this afternoon, I noted the telltale signs.

DR. WHOOPSON: You're amazing, my dear Homes.

HOMES: Of course. (HOMES *waves his fingers before* SLIPCOVER's *face, claps his hands twice, and then snaps his fingers.*)

SLIPCOVER (*Awakening*): Henrietta?

HOMES: Not your wife, my dear fellow. I am Shellack Homes.

SLIPCOVER: Oh, yes, it is Mr. Homes, isn't it? (*Looking around in bewilderment*) What am I doing here?

HOMES: You are the victim of a dastardly plot, Slipcover. But those who are trying to implicate you in their heinous crimes now have to reckon with the brain of Shellack Homes.

DR. WHOOPSON: Hear! Hear!

SLIPCOVER: Plot? But I don't understand—

HOMES: You will, my man. You will. But now, for the good of all, you had best return to your room. Say nothing about our little meeting. And do not worry about sleepwalking. You never will walk in your sleep again.

SLIPCOVER: Oh thank you, Mr. Homes. Thank you. I was becoming a mere shell of my former self. Sleepwalking is a dangerous business. Why, I might have killed myself on one of these nightly expeditions.

HOMES: Exactly.

SLIPCOVER: Well, sir, I'll follow your advice and go to my room. (*Goes toward exit right and stops in doorway*) I think, sir, that I am beginning to know who has caused all this.

HOMES (*Holding up a warning hand*): Say no more, Slipcover, say no more. I am sure you do know. It may interest you to hear that I knew the complete story less than fifteen minutes after I arrived this afternoon.

SLIPCOVER: You're a remarkable man, Mr. Homes.

HOMES: I agree with you.

SLIPCOVER: Well, thank you—and goodnight. (SLIPCOVER *exits.*)

HOMES (*Rubbing his hands together gleefully*): Ah, Whoopson, everything is progressing just as I had hoped.

DR. WHOOPSON (*Scratching his head in bewilderment*): I must confess, my dear Homes, that I'm still very much in the dark.

HOMES (*Laughing*): And yet the entire solution is before your very nose. Ah, Whoopson, Whoopson, you disappoint me. Put that agile mind of yours to work. (HOMES *returns to the divan where he sits.*)

DR. WHOOPSON: You are expecting more visitors? (*Strange, animal-like cries are suddenly heard from offstage.*)

HOMES (*Chuckling*): Aha! Just as I expected!

DR. WHOOPSON: Great heavens, Homes. Those cries are enough to chill even the least susceptible spine.

HOMES (*Still chuckling*): My spine is immune, my dear Whoopson.

DR. WHOOPSON: But hadn't we better investigate?

HOMES: No need. All is well, I assure you. (*Listening intently*) Ah, our visitors will arrive soon, my dear Whoopson. I must ask you to hide behind that chair. (*Points to chair at downstage right.*) I shall place myself behind this divan. Make no noise, Whoopson, and reveal yourself only when I whistle twice.

DR. WHOOPSON (*Still bewildered*): If you say so, Homes. But I'm all in a muddle.

HOMES: So is everyone—except me, my dear Whoopson. (WHOOPSON *hides behind chair.* HOMES *hides behind divan. There is a silence for a moment or two. Then* MONTY DARE *and* ALICE PADDLECART *enter upstage center door, and come to center.*)

MONTY: Beautifully done, was it not, Alice? I uttered those cries under Hermione's window. She'll be shaking with fright.

ALICE: Oh, Monty, you're so clever!

MONTY (*Embracing her*): You're not half bad yourself. You got the pearl?

ALICE: Yes, Mrs. Anguish had hidden this one in a bottle of perfume in her bureau.

MONTY (*Laughing*): The old girl doesn't have much imagination, does she?

ALICE: She's almost as dumb as Hermione.

MONTY: Just think, Alice. If we can pilfer only two more

of the pearls, we can sell them for a small fortune to a good friend of mine in London—Squealy Gore. He's a well-known fence. And then, you and I can go off together to South America to a new life—

ALICE: And to love.

MONTY (*Embracing her again*): Yes, above all, to love. And I'll be free of that weak and simpering Hermione. Why, I wouldn't marry her if she were the last girl in the world. But her mother's pearls will certainly be useful. (HOMES *whistles twice.* DR. WHOOPSON *jumps from behind the chair.* HOMES *reveals himself from behind the divan.*)

HOMES (*Bowing*): A cordial good evening to you, Miss Paddlecart, and to you, Mr. Monty Dare.

MONTY: Curses! Discovered!

ALICE: Oh, we are lost!

DR. WHOOPSON: You're a fine pair of rascals, I must say.

HOMES: Your conniving has been brought to light, Dare. It may interest you to know that I knew the truth about your plotting less than fifteen minutes after I arrived today.

MONTY (*His vanity wounded*): In a pig's eye, you did.

HOMES: Ah, you doubt my word, do you?

MONTY: You bet I do.

HOMES: Very well, my man, then listen. Are you not the son of Danbury Dare?

MONTY: What if I am?

HOMES: Only this. It is well-known that Danbury Dare has long been a student of hypnotism. In fact, he was introduced to its mysteries, as I was, by Professor Longdoze.

MONTY (*Nastily*): And what does that prove?

HOMES: It struck me as very likely that your father would initiate you into the fundamentals of hypnotism. Then when I examined Slipcover's eyes today, it was obvious he had been hypnotized; under your hypnosis, he was forced by you to walk in his sleep, in order, I am sure, that suspicion of the thefts, the nightly noises, and the barn burning might fall on him. (MR. *and* MRS. ANGUISH, *in night clothes, enter hurriedly at right and come to center.*)

MR. ANGUISH: We heard voices here and wondered what was happening.

DR. WHOOPSON: Homes has uncovered the culprits, sir.

HOMES: Exactly. Miss Paddlecart and Mr. Dare have been engaged in a nefarious scheme to rob you of your pearls, madam, and to sell them. Then with their ill-gotten gold, they were going together to South America.

MR. ANGUISH: You cad, Dare—you unspeakable cad!

MONTY: Easy, grandpa, nobody's proved anything yet.

HOMES: Indeed? Whoopson, will you fetch Slipcover at once?

DR. WHOOPSON: Glad to, Homes. (WHOOPSON *exits.*)

HOMES: I first became aware of the fact that Mr. Dare and Miss Paddlecart were more than mere acquaintances this afternoon when he placed his hand on her shoulder.

MONTY: Hmmph!

HOMES: Hmmph me no hmmphs, Dare. The time for retribution is upon you.

MRS. ANGUISH: Oh, Mr. Homes, we owe you a great deal.

HOMES: Naturally, madam, naturally. You will receive a bill for my fee in the morning mail. I detest taking money for my services—but one must live.

MRS. ANGUISH: Of course. (DR. WHOOPSON *enters at right, followed by* SLIPCOVER, MRS. SLIPCOVER, *and* HERMIONE)

HERMIONE (*Rushes to* MONTY *and slaps his face*): Dr. Whoopson has told me all. Oh, how could you, Monty, how could you? (*She bursts into tears.* DR. WHOOPSON *puts a friendly hand around her shoulders and tries to comfort her.*)

HOMES: Ah, Slipcover. Will you tell your story so that Mr. Dare will be revealed for the base fellow he is.

SLIPCOVER: Indeed I will, sir, and glad I am to do it. Since Mr. Dare has been here, he has taken it on himself to visit me often in the kitchen. We talked a great deal, and I noticed that he always looked me straight in the eyes. I thought nothing of it at first, but now I know he was hypnotizing me.

HOMES: Splendid! Splendid! And now, Dare, do you not have an uncle, your father's brother, I believe, named Hubert Dare.

MONTY: What if I do?

HOMES: Nothing, except that he is a confirmed pyromaniac.

MRS. SLIPCOVER: Oh, goodness gracious, and what's that?

HOMES: A pyromaniac, Mrs. Slipcover, is someone who gets great joy out of setting fires.

HERMIONE: How horrible!

HOMES: Exactly. Now let me quote—I have, of course, a photographic memory—from a book by Dr. Pickleman Brine. Here is the quotation. "Of all obsessions, pyromania is the most likely to be inherited. It is known to pass particularly from uncle to nephew, and there are many striking examples to illustrate this fact." End of quotation. Do I make myself clear?

DR. WHOOPSON: Why, dash it, Homes, you mean that young Dare here has inherited pyromania from his uncle and that is why he burned the barn?

HOMES: How well you put these things, Whoopson. Yes, that is exactly the case. I suspect that our poor friend, Slipcover, because of his sleepwalking, was meant to take the blame for that, too.

HERMIONE: Oh, Monty, say it isn't true!

HOMES: I am afraid, miss, that he can say nothing of the kind.

HERMIONE: And, Alice, I trusted you so, and look what you have done. (*She slaps* ALICE's *face.*)

ALICE: Ouch!

MRS. SLIPCOVER: You're a Jezebel, that's what you are. (*She also slaps* ALICE's *face.*)

ALICE: Ouch!

MRS. ANGUISH: And a thief as well. (*She slaps* ALICE's *face.*)

ALICE: Ouch!

MONTY: You won't get me, I can tell you. (*He makes a dash for upstage center door.* HOMES, *with the agility of a panther, is after him at once. He catches* MONTY *just as* MONTY *gets to the door, and, with the flat of his hand, strikes* MONTY *once on the shoulder and once on the neck.* MONTY *falls to the floor howling with pain.*)

HOMES: I am indebted to my old and valued Japanese friend, Haganura Sukiyama, for teaching me the ancient art of jiu-jitsu. It has served me well on many occasions.

MRS. SLIPCOVER (*Admiringly*): Is there anything the man can't do!

HOMES (*Bowing*): Nothing, madam. And now, Dare, and you, Miss Paddlecart, may step outside. I took the liberty of informing my friend, Inspector Bulge of Scotland Yard, that I would have two guests for him tonight. He awaits you out there. Whoopson, will you escort this desperate duo to the waiting arms of Inspector Bulge?

DR. WHOOPSON: A pleasure, my dear fellow. (WHOOPSON *takes* ALICE's *arm. He walks her over to* MONTY, *lifts* MONTY *from floor and takes his arm, and leads both through upstage center door.*)

MR. ANGUISH: Mr. Homes, you are a genius.

HOMES: You are right.

MRS. SLIPCOVER: I've never seen anything like it.

HERMIONE: We are, of course, grateful to you, Mr. Homes. But (*She begins to weep.*) I have lost a fiancé and been completely disillusioned in the bargain.

HOMES: Have no qualms, my dear Miss Anguish. I think of everything. Have you ever heard of Handsome Hogan?

HERMIONE: You mean the young and brilliant Scotland Yard detective who is really the son of an Irish peer, Sir Haphazard Hogan?

HOMES: None other than he.

HERMIONE: Oh!

HOMES: He has told me many times that he is looking for a delicate, fragile, and beautiful girl—object matrimony. I took the liberty, if you will pardon me, of asking him here tonight. And here, if my eyes do not mistake me, is Handsome Hogan with Dr. Whoopson. (DR. WHOOPSON *enters, followed by a tall, handsome young man.*)

DR. WHOOPSON: I've safely delivered the two culprits to Inspector Bulge's waiting arms, Homes.

HOMES: Splendid.

HANDSOME (*Coming to* HERMIONE): And you are Hermione? (*He gazes at her rapturously.*)

HERMIONE (*Also enraptured*): And you are Handsome Hogan.

HANDSOME: Forgive me for the suggestion—I know it is late—but would you stroll with me in the garden.

HERMIONE: Oh, bother the time of night! I'd love to. (*Hand in hand, they exit upstage center.*)

MRS. SLIPCOVER: Isn't that a beautiful sight, though?

HOMES: Ah, yes, young love, young love. And now that all difficulties are cleared, I shall seek relaxation in the solace of my violin. (*He goes to side of divan, picks up case, removes violin and bow, and sits down on divan. The others, with the exception of* DR. WHOOPSON, *exchange agonized looks.*) You are all welcome to stay. (*He begins his playing, making horrible sounds.*)

MRS. ANGUISH: It's lovely and all that, Mr. Homes, but I think I'd like a cup of tea. (*She exits hastily right.*)

MR. ANGUISH: I'm a great music lover, Homes, and I appreciate your invitation, but I could do with a spot of tea myself. (*He exits hurriedly right.*)

SLIPCOVER: I'd dearly love to stay, but my sleepwalking activities have wearied me. I think it best I retire. (*He runs to exit.*)

MRS. SLIPCOVER: Slipcover may need me. (*She hastily exits right.*)

DR. WHOOPSON: Too bad they couldn't stay, Homes— you're in unusually good form tonight.

HOMES (*Over the squeaks and groans of his horrendous fiddling*): Ah, yes, Whoopson, music hath charms. (WHOOPSON *gazes at him in great admiration as the curtain falls.*)

THE END

Production Notes

THE CASE OF THE MISSING PEARLS

Characters: 6 male; 4 female.

Playing Time: 30 minutes.

Costumes: Shellack Homes is dressed in traditional costume of Sherlock Holmes: cape, peaked, plaid hat with bow on top, pipe almost continually in his mouth, etc. Others wear costumes in style in the Victorian period. In Scene 2, Mr. and Mrs. Anguish wear night clothes and bathrobes.

Properties: Violin case and violin; magnifying glass; vase of flowers; magazines; cigarette ashes on a slip of paper.

Setting: The living room of Buxton Anguish. The room is furnished luxuriously, in late Victorian style. At upstage center is a door leading onto terrace. There are windows right and left of this door. In the center of the room, there is a table on which are several magazines and a vase of spring flowers. Comfortable chairs stand at right and left of table, and a large divan downstage left. There is a large easy chair downstage right. On right wall is a well-stocked bookcase. On left wall is a door leading to another room.

Lighting: No special effects.

Strong and Silent

Characters

PECOS JOE, *a slim, wiry, rather garrulous cowhand*
INJUN PETE, *a good Indian*
ANNIE, *plump and bustling cook at the Bar Nothing Ranch*
TRIGGER SAM, *foreman of the Bar Nothing*
LYDIA SAGEBRUSH, *young, attractive owner of the Bar Nothing*
JED WEDGEWOOD, *the strong and silent hero*
MARIE LAPORTE, *a young woman entertainer*

SCENE 1

TIME: *An afternoon in the days of the Wild West.*
SETTING: *The bunkhouse of the Bar Nothing Ranch.*
AT RISE: PECOS JOE *is lying on cot at left, singing "Home on the Range" in a rather tuneless voice.* INJUN PETE *sits in chair at right of table with his arms crossed, staring into space.*

PECOS JOE: "Home, home on the range,
  Where the deer and the antelope play;
  Where seldom is heard
  A discouraging word,
  And the skies are not cloudy all day."
INJUN PETE: Ugh! That good song—but voice very bad.

PECOS JOE: Says you, Injun Pete.

INJUN PETE: I tell you, Pecos Joe, better you think about song but don't sing it.

PECOS JOE: You're an insultin' Injun. Where I come from they think I've got a good voice.

INJUN PETE: Where you come from must be plenty bad singers.

PECOS JOE: Look, Injun Pete, I'm a rip-snortin', gun-totin' bronco buster. I've got the heart of a bear and the fangs of a coyote. And I've got a voice to charm the birds off the trees.

INJUN PETE: Ugh!

PECOS JOE: And a hearty ugh to you. (ANNIE, *the cook, enters at upstage center.*)

ANNIE: Howdy, Pecos. Howdy, Injun Pete. Trigger Sam back yet?

PECOS JOE: Haven't seen him.

ANNIE: Well, as foreman of this here Bar Nothing Ranch, he's got another problem to face.

PECOS JOE: Don't tell me them ornery rustlers have been at it again.

INJUN PETE: Rustlers, ugh!

ANNIE: You said it, Injun Pete. They got another twenty head of cattle last night up in the south pasture.

PECOS JOE: I'd like to get my hands on those dirty crooks! I'm the fastest man on the draw in Cawcawgawcaw County. I've the heart of lion and the temper of a tiger. I've—

ANNIE: Yeah, we know all about that, Pecos. But seems as if you're just never around when these things happen. Where were you last night, anyway?

PECOS JOE: Down to the town with a few of the boys.

ANNIE: At the Last Chance Saloon, I'll bet. Bending your

elbow and listenin' to that hussy, Marie LaPorte, sing her silly head off.

PECOS JOE: You haven't any call to run down Marie, Annie.

ANNIE: I wouldn't trust her as far as I could throw her. She's a varmint if I ever saw one.

PECOS JOE: You wouldn't be jealous, would you, Annie?

ANNIE: Jealous? That's a laugh!

PECOS JOE: How's the boss lady takin' the latest news about the rustlers?

ANNIE: She's upset, as who wouldn't be? Why, she must have lost nearly a hundred head of cattle in the last month. She's a brave girl, is Lydia Sagebrush, but she has too much to bear on her pretty shoulders. Don't seem right that a mere slip of a girl like her should have to run a ranch as all-fired big as the Bar Nothing. But since her Pa died, that's what she's had to do. And her Ma ain't much help; she's gettin' more feeble every day.

PECOS JOE: Wish there was somethin' I could do.

ANNIE: You might try stayin' around nights and keepin' your eyes open.

PECOS JOE: I have the eyes of an eagle.

ANNIE: And you use 'em to stare at that Marie LaPorte. Well, breakfast is near ready at the main house. I've cooked you some flapjacks, bacon, eggs, ham, hot biscuits, apple pie, doughnuts, and steamin' coffee.

PECOS JOE: Well, it'll be a light snack until dinner time. I've got the appetite of a wolf and the teeth of a panther.

ANNIE: And the brain of a doodle-bug. (TRIGGER SAM SNELL, *foreman of the Bar Nothing Ranch, enters at center. He walks to table, pours a little water from pitcher into bowl, and washes his face. He dries it on a towel which is hanging on a hook near* PECOS JOE's *cot.*)

TRIGGER SAM: It's hot out there on the range. But I wanted to get a couple of things done before breakfast.

ANNIE: Them rustlers were here again last night.

TRIGGER SAM: I know. I saw their tracks down at the south pasture this mornin'.

ANNIE: Seems to me that if you and some of the boys had been down there last night, keepin' watch the way you ought to, you might have caught the ornery coyotes.

TRIGGER SAM (*Wiping face briskly*): I can't be everywhere at once, Annie.

PECOS JOE: Sam was with me last night, anyway.

ANNIE: I thought so. That Marie LaPorte attracts all you lame-brained men.

TRIGGER SAM: It was the first night off I've taken in a coon's age.

ANNIE: Well, it was the wrong night—as usual. (LYDIA SAGEBRUSH, *owner of the Bar Nothing Ranch, enters at center, followed by* JED WEDGEWOOD, *our hero. He is chewing slowly on a wad of gum.*)

LYDIA: Oh, there you are, Trigger Sam. I've been looking for you. You've heard about the rustlers?

TRIGGER SAM: I heard.

LYDIA: Alas, what are we to do? If they come here much more, we won't have any cattle left at all. Oh, if Daddy were only alive.

ANNIE: It was a sad day for us all when he passed into the Great Beyond.

LYDIA: When he headed for the Last Round-up, we little knew how severe was our loss.

INJUN PETE: Big loss. Boss was heap fine man.

LYDIA: Before I forget, Sam, this is Jed Wedgewood. I've just hired him, because I thought we could use another hand.

JED (*Chewing slowly*): Howdy.

TRIGGER SAM: Another man, eh? (*To* JED) You had experience as a cowhand?

JED: Yep.

TRIGGER SAM: Can you rope, bust a bronco, use brandin' irons, ride tall in the saddle?

JED: Yep.

TRIGGER SAM: Ain't much for talkin', are you?

JED: Nope.

TRIGGER SAM: How are you on the draw?

JED (*Whipping gun quickly from holster*): Middlin'.

PECOS JOE: Say. That looked pretty fast to me. And I'm the gosh-dangest, lightnin'-fastest, trigger-fingered galoot in Cawcawgawcaw County.

INJUN PETE: Ugh!

TRIGGER SAM: He know all about the rustlin' trouble we been havin', Boss?

LYDIA: I told him the job might be dangerous and that the boys take turns at night keeping watch. That is—all except last night. I still don't understand that, Trigger Sam.

TRIGGER SAM: Well, things had been quiet for so long, Pecos and me thought we could risk a night in town.

ANNIE: You sure calculated wrong.

TRIGGER SAM: Anyway, we can use this fellow, I reckon. (*Points to cot at right.*) You can bed down there.

JED: Right.

ANNIE: And breakfast is ready. So you boys had better come up to the house.

PECOS JOE: We'll be there.

ANNIE: I'm not worryin' about *that!* (*She exits at center.*)

LYDIA (*To* JED): I hope you'll like it with us.

JED: Likely.

LYDIA (*Goes to center door*): After breakfast, Trigger Sam, I want to talk to you.

TRIGGER SAM: O.K., Boss. (*Exit* LYDIA. TRIGGER SAM *turns to* JED.) You can bring in your gear after we eat. Time to put on the feedbag now. You'll like Annie's cookin'.

JED (*Still chewing*): Good.

TRIGGER SAM: Well, let's get goin'. (*He exits at center followed by* JED.)

PECOS JOE: Ready for eats, Injun Pete?

INJUN PETE: Heap ready.

PECOS JOE: Then off we go. I've got the appetite of a mountain lion and the capacity of a rogue elephant. (*He rises from cot, moves toward door, and begins to sing tunelessly "Home on the Range."*)

INJUN PETE (*With obvious distress*): Ugh! (*They exit as the curtains close.*)

* * * *

SCENE 2

TIME: *Later the same afternoon.*

SETTING: *The bunkhouse.*

AT RISE: JED *is seated at left of table, whistling softly and cleaning his gun. This done, he places it in his holster. Then, he takes a piece of paper from his pocket, reads it, smiles, and replaces it. The center door opens suddenly, and* MARIE LAPORTE *enters, walking somewhat provocatively.*

MARIE: Well, say. Hello, handsome. You're new around these parts, aren't you?

JED: Yep.

MARIE: You certainly make the place look brighter. What do they call you, handsome?

JED: Jed.

MARIE: Jed, huh. A nice friendly sort of name. Anything go with it?

JED: Wedgewood.

MARIE: Jed Wedgewood. Well, I'm Marie LaPorte. I sing down at the Last Chance Saloon. (*Invitingly*) Drop down some time, big boy.

JED: Thanks.

MARIE: Trigger Sam and Pecos not around?

JED: Nope.

MARIE: Say, you don't waste any words, do you, handsome? Well, that's the way I like 'em—tall, strong, and silent. (*Coyly touching his arm*) Mmmm . . . muscles of iron!

JED: Yep.

MARIE: I thought I'd drive over today to tell the boys we're having a real shindig tonight at the Last Chance. Smiley Brown, who owns the joint, is celebrating his birthday. And let me tell you, handsome, when Smiley celebrates, he celebrates with a capital "C"—or is it "S"? I never was much of a one for spelling.

JED: "C."

MARIE: Thanks. You're a big help. I hope you come tonight, too. You're just what the party needs. (ANNIE *enters at center with mop in her hand.*)

ANNIE: I thought I'd come over and clean the place up a bit before supper. (*Seeing* MARIE) Oh, it's you. What are you doing here, Marie LaPorte?

MARIE: Hello, Annie, you old warhorse, how are you? You don't sound very friendly.

ANNIE: Why should I be? We had rustlers here again last night, while the boys were down to the Last Chance listening to your dad-blamed foolishness.

MARIE: I've got a good voice, Annie. You ought to hear it.

Do you good to get away from the Bar Nothing for a change.

ANNIE: The Last Chance Saloon never did anybody any good.

MARIE (*Laughing*): Don't be funny.

ANNIE: I'm not being funny. I always remember what my old grandma used to say, "Lips that touch liquor shall never touch mine."

MARIE: She sounds like quite an old girl.

ANNIE: She was worth twenty of your kind.

MARIE (*Angrily*): Now look here, Annie. I didn't come over here spoiling for a brawl.

ANNIE: But you'll get one if you stay around here much longer.

MARIE: It's a free country. I've got a right to come and go as I please.

ANNIE (*Advancing menacingly on* MARIE *with mop in air*): I've got a mind to land this right on your dyed head. (TRIGGER SAM *and* PECOS JOE *enter at center followed by* INJUN PETE.)

TRIGGER SAM: What's goin' on here, Annie? Leave Marie alone.

MARIE: All a girl does is try to pay a friendly little visit, and this old witch wants to bang her on the noggin.

PECOS JOE: Be a lady, Annie.

ANNIE (*Lowering mop*): Lady! That's a good one. A lot you know about ladies after traipsin' down to town to listen to the likes of this one.

INJUN PETE: She bad squaw.

TRIGGER SAM: What's on your mind, Marie?

MARIE: Smiley Brown's celebratin' his birthday tonight down at the Last Chance. He wants you boys to be on hand.

TRIGGER SAM: Now, that's real nice of Smiley. He's a friendly sort of galoot.

MARIE: And everything will be on the house.

PECOS JOE: I've the thirst of a camel and the—

ANNIE: And the courage of a weasel.

PECOS JOE: Look here, Annie. You haven't any call to say that.

ANNIE: Suppose them rustlers come back tonight? (LYDIA SAGEBRUSH *enters at center*.)

LYDIA: Oh, there you are, Trigger Sam. Who's going to be on watch tonight?

ANNIE: There ain't nobody goin' to be on watch, Lydia. These coyotes will all be down at the Last Chance.

INJUN PETE: Ugh! Bad medicine!

LYDIA: At the Last Chance! But, Trigger Sam, you know there is danger from the rustlers. Someone must be here.

TRIGGER SAM: They'd never come back two nights in a row. They never have.

PECOS JOE: Trigger Sam's right. They won't be pushin' their luck.

MARIE: You've got nothin' to worry about, kid.

LYDIA: Oh, what am I to do! If Daddy were only alive!

JED: I'm here, ma'am.

MARIE: Oh, listen now, handsome. (*Goes over to him and gives him an alluring look*) You'll want to be in on the fun, too. Trigger Sam's right. Rustlers would never come back two nights in a row.

PECOS JOE: Marie's right, Boss.

TRIGGER SAM: Sure she is.

LYDIA: Then nothing I can say will make you listen to the call of duty?

TRIGGER SAM: I know my duty, Boss, but I tell you, there'll be no rustlers tonight.

LYDIA: Alas, this is a black hour.

JED (*Chewing thoughtfully*): I'm here, ma'am.

MARIE: You boys have made the right decision. And I hope you change your mind, handsome. (*Coyly*) Any of you galoots want to walk me down to my buggy?

PECOS JOE: A pleasure, Marie.

TRIGGER SAM: Sure thing. (*To* LYDIA) And don't worry, Boss. We know what we're doin'.

MARIE: Then goodbye, all. And a very special goodbye to you, handsome. (MARIE *exits center, followed by* PECOS JOE *and* TRIGGER SAM. LYDIA *comes to center of stage, looking dejected.*)

ANNIE: I was goin' to clean up this dump, but cleanin' is too good for the hogs that live here. Let 'em live in filth. (*She exits.* INJUN JOE *seats himself on cot at right, folds arms, and stares into space.* JED *joins* LYDIA *at center.*)

LYDIA: It's so difficult for a girl to control a group of men. I try and try to make a go of the ranch, but things seem to get worse and worse. I don't know where to turn.

JED: I'm here, ma'am.

LYDIA (*Looking at him as though seeing him for the first time*): Yes, you are. Do you know, Jed, there's something so solid and comfortable about you. You seem like the sort of person I could trust—almost like Daddy.

INJUN PETE: Boss good man. Too bad he go to Happy Hunting Ground.

LYDIA: And will you really be on the watch tonight? Will you go down to the south pasture?

JED: Yep.

LYDIA: I'm beginning to feel safer already. Trigger Sam and Pecos have caught sight of the rustlers a couple of times—but the rustlers always got away.

INJUN PETE: Ugh! Rustlers' horses too fast for us. They went thataway.

LYDIA: But somehow or other, I feel that nobody could get away from you. You're strong and silent, and you seem thoroughly capable.

JED: Yep.

LYDIA: If the rustlers steal much more, I'll be ruined. I'll just have to close the ranch and sell it to Smiley Brown, who owns the Last Chance. He's been after me to sell it for a long time.

JED: Likely.

LYDIA: Why do you say "likely"?

JED: Just thinkin'.

LYDIA (*Taking both his hands in hers*): I'm placing my faith in you, Jed. I feel that I can trust you completely.

JED: You can.

LYDIA: And you'll go to the south pasture at sundown?

JED: Yep.

LYDIA: Thank you, Jed. Thank you. (*She reaches on tiptoe, kisses his cheek, then goes hurriedly, and rather embarrassedly to center door and exits.*)

JED (*Touching the spot where she kissed him*): Shucks.

INJUN PETE: Nice squaw there.

JED: Yep.

INJUN PETE: Injun Pete watch with you tonight.

JED: Thanks.

INJUN PETE: Rustlers! Ugh! Bad medicine. (*JED sits at left of table, begins to whistle softly. He takes out his gun, looks down the barrel, replaces it in holster, and smiles. Then he takes the piece of paper from his pocket, looks at it, and smiles very broadly as the curtains close.*)

* * * *

SCENE 3

TIME: *Late that night.*

SETTING: *The south pasture of the Bar Nothing Ranch.* NOTE: *This scene may be played before the curtain.*

BEFORE RISE: JED *is sitting on ground at center.* INJUN PETE *is seated at right.*

INJUN PETE: Nice night. Plenty stars.

JED: Sure is.

INJUN PETE: Plenty quiet, too.

JED: Yep. (JED *rises and walks to left peering off into the distance. Then he returns to center where he remains standing.*)

INJUN PETE: Maybe boys right. No rustlers tonight.

JED: Maybe. (*Suddenly a slight noise is heard offstage.* JED *puts hand to holster and goes slowly toward left.* INJUN PETE *rises and advances slowly, too, toward left. Suddenly a figure hurls himself at* JED *from left. The two grapple on the ground.* JED *emerges as victor, then takes a piece of rope and ties his assailant's hands behind his back.* INJUN PETE *watches approvingly. Horses' hoofs are heard offstage.*)

JED: Sit on him, Injun Pete.

INJUN PETE (*Complying with the request*): Heap pleasure.

JED: I'll go after the others. (*He exits hurriedly at left, his gun drawn. After a moment, there is the sound of gunfire offstage.*)

INJUN PETE: Ugh! Rustlers! Bad medicine! (*He rises and drags assailant offstage.*)

*   *   *   *

Scene 4

Time: *About an hour later.*

Setting: *The bunkhouse.*

At Rise: Jed *is standing at center with* Lydia *beside him.* Injun Pete *is sitting in his customary pose on cot at right. In chair at left of table, his hands bound behind him, is* Trigger Sam. Pecos Joe, *looking completely bewildered, is seated on cot at left.* Annie *is standing near* Injun Pete.

Pecos Joe: Say it ain't true, Trigger Sam.

Annie: It's true all right. He's a low-down, crawlin', poisonous, no-good, snivellin' snake.

Pecos Joe: I've got the heart of a lion and the courage of a jaguar, but it's a real blow to a man when he finds that his best friend is a dirty rustler.

Injun Pete: Heap dirty. Me sit on him good.

Lydia: How can I ever thank you enough, Jed. To think of all you've done for us tonight! And almost single-handed— (Injun Pete *coughs.*) I mean, of course, with Injun Pete's help. And you've already taken the four others to the town jail and delivered them to Sheriff Blake. You're so strong and silent and wonderful—

Annie: He sure is!

Injun Pete: He ride like wind and shoot like Sitting Bull.

Jed: Shucks, ma'am.

Lydia: And you're so modest about it.

Jed (*Takes paper from pocket and hands it to* Lydia): Better read this, ma'am.

Lydia (*Looking at paper*): A United States Government seal! Why, Jed! (*She begins to read aloud.*) "This is to certify that Jed Wedgewood is a properly appointed United

States marshal whose special duty is to investigate the increase in cattle rustling in Cawcawgawcaw County. Mr. Wedgewood, a graduate of Harvard University, is to receive the full cooperation of all law officials wherever his work takes him. Signed—James A. Garfield, President of the United States." Oh, Jed.

PECOS JOE: President Garfield!

ANNIE: A Harvard man!

JED: So now that you know who I really am, perhaps I may be allowed to assume my real identity. I am not normally so laconic as I have led you to believe.

ANNIE: Listen to them big words! He's a Harvard man all right!

PECOS JOE: He's got the tongue of a nightingale and the industry of a beaver.

JED: You see, from the first time I set foot in this bunkhouse, I sensed that something was amiss. In the first place, this trip of Trigger Sam to town the other night seemed entirely unnecessary. After all, why should a responsible foreman of a ranch leave that ranch when he knew there was danger from rustlers?

TRIGGER SAM (*Bitterly*): Well, you know now.

ANNIE: You bet we do, you low-down, sneakin', creepin' apology for a man!

JED: Then, Miss Sagebrush—

LYDIA: Please call me Lydia, Jed.

JED (*Smiling*): Very well then, Lydia. When Marie LaPorte showed up here and was so insistent that Trigger Sam, Pecos, and I should go down to the Last Chance tonight, I really began to suspect something.

LYDIA: Oh, Jed, you're so brilliant!

INJUN PETE: Plenty smart fellow!

JED: Then when you told me that Smiley Brown, the proprietor of the Last Chance, has wanted to buy the Bar Nothing Ranch, I began to see the light. It was obvious that Smiley was responsible for the rustling, that he wanted to frighten you, Lydia, into letting him have the ranch. It was obvious, too, that someone here was working with him. That someone proved to be Trigger Sam. You see, every time Trigger Sam went down to the Last Chance, it was the signal for Smiley and his men to come here. They knew nobody would be around. Trigger Sam was being paid off by Smiley.

ANNIE: Trigger, you're a loathsome rat!

TRIGGER SAM: Well, we almost got away with it.

JED: When Trigger and Smiley knew I would be on watch tonight, it was Trigger's job to get rid of me. As you know, he failed.

ANNIE: And what about that Marie LaPorte? Was the hussy in on it, too?

JED: I don't know. Perhaps she was, and perhaps she wasn't.

PECOS JOE: Oh, Marie's all right. She's a diamond in the rough, that's all.

ANNIE: She may be rough, but she ain't no diamond!

JED: And that's the story.

LYDIA (*Looking at* JED *with shining eyes*): Oh, if Daddy were only alive! He'd be proud to know you! As proud, Jed, as I am.

JED: Thank you, Miss Sage—I mean Lydia.

PECOS JOE (*Rising and coming over to* JED): I'd like to shake your hand, Jed. I've got the bravery of a lion myself, and I admire the same quality in others.

ANNIE: Listen to him!

JED (*Shaking hands*): Thank you, Pecos. And now I'd like to ask a favor of you.

PECOS JOE: Anything at all, pardner.

JED: I'd like you and Injun Pete to take Trigger Sam down
to the jail so that he can join the rest of his pals.

PECOS JOE: It'll be a pleasure.

INJUN PETE (*Rising and going toward* TRIGGER SAM): Heap
big pleasure.

TRIGGER SAM: Don't let that Injun get his hands on me!

PECOS JOE: Don't worry, Trigger. The Injun's as gentle as
a lamb and as mild as spring rain.

TRIGGER SAM: You wouldn't think so if he'd been sittin' on
you for half an hour. (PECOS JOE *and* INJUN PETE *take*
TRIGGER SAM *by the arms and lead him firmly toward center
door. At door,* TRIGGER SAM *turns for one final glare at* JED.)
I ain't likely to be forgettin' this, Mr. United States
Marshal. If you and me ever meet up again, you'd better
be ready.

JED (*Quietly*): I'll be ready, Trigger Sam. (TRIGGER SAM,
PECOS JOE, *and* INJUN PETE *exit.*)

ANNIE (*Yawning*): I'll be gettin' up to the house. I ain't
used to these late hours. (*Coming to* JED) Shake, friend.
You're one in a million.

JED: Thank you, Annie. You're not so bad yourself. (ANNIE
exits.)

LYDIA: Jed, how can I ever thank you? You've saved my
ranch and brought security to all of us.

JED (*Reverting to original character*): Shucks, ma'am.

LYDIA (*Laughing*): Oh, Jed—not that again! (*Seriously*) Can
you stay on with us, Jed? I'll need a new foreman now
that Trigger Sam has been revealed for what he is. I can't
think of anyone better for the job than you.

JED (*Rather sadly*): I appreciate the offer, Lydia, but the
answer is in that piece of paper you've just read. I still
have a job to do. There are other ranches in the county
that need my help against rustlers.

LYDIA: You mean you can't stay?

JED: I'm sorry, Lydia. But tomorrow at dawn, I'll have to be riding off on Old Paint into the sunrise. Duty calls from beyond the hills. (*Determinedly*) And no Harvard man would shirk his duty.

LYDIA: And you'll never come back?

JED (*Warmly*): I didn't say that, Lydia. Some day—I can't say just when—'long about sunset, you'll see a lone rider coming along the range.

LYDIA: And you'll be the rider?

JED: Yep.

LYDIA (*Rapturously*): Oh, Jed.

JED: Because my heart will always be here.

LYDIA: You really mean that, Jed?

JED: Yep.

LYDIA: And you'll be going tomorrow then?

JED: But there's still tonight. There's no law that says we can't go out and look at the stars.

LYDIA: That would be lovely.

JED (*Taking her hand*): Then let's go. (*They walk hand in hand toward center door.*)

LYDIA: I hope that sunset and the lone rider come soon, Jed.

JED: They'll come, Lydia. They'll come. I promise you. (*Loudly and determinedly*) And a Harvard man never breaks his word! (*They exit center as the curtains close.*)

THE END

Production Notes

STRONG AND SILENT

Characters: 4 male; 3 female.

Playing Time: 30 minutes.

Costumes: Pecos Joe, Trigger Sam, and Jed Wedgewood wear traditional cowboy costumes. Injun Pete wears a large blanket and a felt hat with feather in it. Lydia Sagebrush wears blue jeans, boots, and an attractive sweater. Annie wears a large bright apron over her plain cotton dress. Marie LaPorte wears gaudy theatrical clothes and jewelry.

Properties: Gun, rope, and document for Jed; mop for Annie; mask for Trigger Sam.

Setting: Scenes 1, 2, and 4 take place in the bunkhouse of the Bar Nothing Ranch. There is a door at upstage center, and small windows to either side of the door. In the middle of the room is a crude table with a pitcher and washbowl on it. Two chairs flank this table. There are two cots, one at left wall and one at right wall. A towel hangs on a nail above cot at left. Scene 3 may be played before the curtain. A few shrubs and rocks may be scattered around the scene, if desired, to suggest a Western setting.

Lighting: No special effects necessary. If desired, lights may be dimmed in Scene 3, to suggest night.

Sound: Sounds of horses' hoofs and gunfire offstage, as indicated in text.

118

Out of This World

Characters

MRS. SAYERS
IRENE SAYERS, *an attractive girl about 22*
JILL SAYERS, *her sister, about 16*
LYDIA, *the maid*
CLIVE NORCROSS, *a friend of Irene's*
BILL BARNES, *about 17*

TIME: *An early evening in late May.*
SETTING: *The living room of the Sayers' home.*
AT RISE: LYDIA, *the maid, is dusting a table. She is humming a popular tune.* MRS. SAYERS *enters.*

MRS. SAYERS (*Coming to table*): I thought you did the dusting early this morning, Lydia.

LYDIA: I did, Mrs. Sayers. (*She continues her humming.*)

MRS. SAYERS: Then why this sudden burst of night work?

LYDIA (*Going over to bookcase and beginning to remove each book and to dust it separately*): Well, ma'am, Miss Irene told me she wanted the house to be spick-and-span tonight. (*She goes on humming.*)

MRS. SAYERS (*Rearranging flowers in vase*): Oh, she did? And why is Irene so particular about tonight?

LYDIA: Mr. Norcross is coming.

MRS. SAYERS: Well, I must say that Clive Norcross is getting to be a very frequent visitor, isn't he?

LYDIA: Yes, ma'am, that he is. And he's a cute trick, if you ask me.

MRS. SAYERS: Yes, Clive seems to be a very nice boy. (LYDIA *continues her humming.*)

MRS. SAYERS: What in the world is that tune you're so fond of?

LYDIA: Isn't it out of this world? And you'll never guess who I heard sing it last night—in person at the Empire Theater!

MRS. SAYERS (*Smiling*): Well, tell me. This suspense is positively killing.

LYDIA: Terry Bromo!

MRS. SAYERS: Terry Bromo? Who on earth is Terry Bromo? Sounds like a headache powder!

LYDIA: Why, Mrs. Sayers, I'm surprised at you! Terry Bromo is positively the world's crooniest crooner! (*She sighs*) He's got curly dark hair, blue eyes, and a lovely tan! When he sings, he crinkles up his nose like a rabbit.

MRS. SAYERS: That must be fascinating.

LYDIA: It's out of this world!

MRS. SAYERS (*Seating herself at table*): Where's Jill?

LYDIA: She's studying up in her room.

MRS. SAYERS: Well, that's a pleasant change. It seems to me that she's been neglecting her work lately. When I was sixteen, I spent much more time on my studies.

LYDIA (*Laughing*): When you were sixteen, you didn't have a crush on Bill Barnes!

MRS. SAYERS: Bill Barnes! You mean that boy who's so infatuated with Irene.

LYDIA: Isn't it a scream—and Miss Irene is at least five years older than Bill.

MRS. SAYERS: No! Since you ask me, I don't think it is a scream at all. It's rather sad, and Irene is very much upset. She doesn't want to hurt young Bill's feelings, but she's getting rather tired of being haunted by him. He just sits and stares at her like a worshiping cow!

LYDIA: It's out of this world!

MRS. SAYERS: It's very much in this world, I'm afraid, and your telling me that Jill has a crush on Bill Barnes only serves to complicate matters more.

LYDIA: Life is a mess sometimes, isn't it? Gosh, I often think I'd like to go to a desert island away from it all.

MRS. SAYERS: Alone?

LYDIA (*After humming a few bars of her tune*): Alone? Gosh, no! With somebody like Terry Bromo! I can just hear him singing to me under tropical palms! (*She runs the dustcloth quickly over the top of the bookcase.*) There, that's done.

MRS. SAYERS (*Laughing*): You certainly are a romantic soul, Lydia!

LYDIA: I sure am! (IRENE SAYERS *enters at stairway right. She is a poised, attractive, well-dressed girl of twenty-two.*)

IRENE: Hi, Mother! Hi, Lydia.

LYDIA: I'll finish up the dinner dishes now. (LYDIA *exits left.* IRENE *seats herself on sofa.*)

IRENE (*Looking at her watch*): Clive ought to be here at any moment now.

MRS. SAYERS: Are you staying in with him or going out?

IRENE: We'll stay in, I suppose, unless Bill Barnes drops in—in which case we'll make a hasty exit.

MRS. SAYERS: Poor Bill! I've been talking with Lydia about him. He's a problem, isn't he?

IRENE (*Sighing*): He certainly is! He's a nice kid, and I wouldn't want to hurt him in any way; but, gosh, he just sits and looks at me as if I were Helen of Troy or the ten most beautiful women in the world!

MRS. SAYERS (*Smiling*): Well, you are attractive, Irene; though I suppose that I, as your mother, shouldn't say so.

IRENE (*Laughing*): You're just prejudiced in my favor, Mother. I think that Jill will grow up to be the beauty in this family.

MRS. SAYERS: Is it true what Lydia just told me about Jill?

IRENE: If Lydia said something, it probably is true. She's got sharp eyes and a sharp ear for crooners, too. What did she say?

MRS. SAYERS: She claims that Jill has a crush on Bill Barnes.

IRENE: She's right. That's what makes the situation even more horrible.

MRS. SAYERS: What does Clive think about the problem?

IRENE: Oh, Clive's as tenderhearted as a chicken. He likes Bill and doesn't want to see him hurt either.

MRS. SAYERS (*Rising from chair and going to bookcase*): Are you and Clive serious about each other, Irene?

IRENE (*Thoughtfully*): Yes, Mother—very serious.

MRS. SAYERS (*Selecting book*): Then something should certainly be done about poor Bill. After all, he's only a boy —seventeen, isn't he?

IRENE: Yes.

MRS. SAYERS (*Shaking her head*): And you're twenty-two— almost twenty-three. (*Returns to chair*) Yours isn't an uncommon problem, you know. Boys of Bill's age often think themselves in love with older girls. (*She seats herself with a smile.*) I could tell a tale or two about your own father when he was Bill's age—

IRENE: Do tell me! Kidding Dad along would be fun!

MRS. SAYERS: No, he'd never forgive me. A man's great weakness is his pride, you know. (JILL SAYERS *enters at stairway right. She is a pretty girl of sixteen, but she enters in listless, dejected manner. She comes to easy chair and seats herself.)*

IRENE: Gosh! Wipe that grin off your face!

MRS. SAYERS: Why, Jill, you look as if you'd just been exiled to Siberia! What's the matter?

JILL: Nothing.

MRS. SAYERS: Is your studying done?

JILL: I suppose so.

IRENE: Just what have you been studying, anyway?

JILL: English. We've been reading Shakespeare's "Julius Caesar." I had to memorize some lines. (*She begins to recite in a dull, listless manner.*)
"Friends, Romans, countrymen, lend me your ears!
I come to bury Caesar not to praise him;
The evil that men do lives after them;
The good is oft interred with their bones—
So let it be with Caesar."

IRENE: Golly! You certainly make it sound like a funeral oration!

JILL: That's what it's supposed to be. (*Dejectedly*) I'm just not in the mood for Willie Shakespeare tonight.

IRENE: If Willie ever heard you recite his lines that way, he certainly wouldn't be in the mood for you, either!

JILL: I suppose not. Is Clive coming tonight?

IRENE: Yes.

MRS. SAYERS: Jill, I want to have a serious talk with you. After all, we've always discussed important problems together. (*She coughs*) I'll come right to the point. Do you like Bill Barnes?

JILL (*Uncomfortably*): Why, Mother! Whoever said I did!

IRENE: Oh, come on, Jill—out with it! It's no crime to like somebody.

JILL (*With a sudden burst of life*): Yes, I do like Bill! But all he ever does is come here and moon around Irene. You'd never know I was around! (IRENE *and* MRS. SAYERS *exchange meaningful glances.*)

MRS. SAYERS: I suppose that accounts for your present mood then. (JILL *nods unhappily.*) But remember, Jill, you're not the first girl who has found herself in such a predicament. These things pass over.

JILL: I suppose they do—but they're awful while they last! (*The doorbell rings.*)

IRENE: That must be Clive.

LYDIA (*From kitchen*): I'll get it! (*She enters from left, goes to door, and opens it.*) Hello, Mr. Norcross. (CLIVE NORCROSS *enters. He is a good-looking, lively young fellow of about* IRENE'S *age.*)

CLIVE: Hello, Lydia. How's the crooner's delight?

LYDIA: Oh, go on, you! You're just jealous of Terry Bromo's appeal. I'll bet you wish they'd swoon for you.

CLIVE (*Laughing*): Sometimes I think it would be rather fun! (*He comes to center*) Hi, everybody. (*To* JILL) Why so glum, chum?

IRENE: Jill is passing through one of life's great sorrows, Clive.

JILL (*Angrily*): It isn't funny, Irene!

MRS. SAYERS: Now, girls! No quarreling!

IRENE (*Penitently*): I'm sorry, Jill. I didn't mean to be nasty. Gosh, all this affects me as much as it does you.

LYDIA: Back to the dishes! No rest for the wicked! (LYDIA *exits left.*)

MRS. SAYERS: I suppose you know how things stand, Clive —I mean about the matter of Bill Barnes.

CLIVE: Yes, I do.

IRENE: Clive knows all about everything—including Jill.

MRS. SAYERS: Well, something certainly ought to be done about it.

LYDIA (*Poking her head through doorway left*): Bill Barnes is headed this way. I just saw him through the kitchen window.

IRENE: Oh, murder!

LYDIA: I wish it were Terry Bromo! (LYDIA *disappears.*)

CLIVE (*Quickly*): You know I've been thinking of a way out of all this, and I've hit upon a plan that might work. Irene, do you remember how you once played the Spirit of Poverty in a school pageant?

IRENE: I'll say I do! I looked like something that had been left out in the rain all night!

CLIVE: Do you folks mind if I whisper something very important to Irene?

MRS. SAYERS (*Rising from chair*): No, go right ahead, mystery man. I'm going upstairs to read. (MRS. SAYERS *exits.*)

JILL (*Rising*): I'd better go back to "Julius Caesar," I suppose. (CLIVE *is now talking softly to* IRENE, *who is giggling excitedly.* JILL *walks listlessly toward stairway.*)

CLIVE: Don't go yet, Jill. (JILL *stops.*)

IRENE: I'll do it! By golly, you've got a brain, Clive!

CLIVE: It's one of my great charms, he replied modestly. (IRENE *exits quickly at stairway right.*)

JILL: Of all the mysterious goings on! It's like something out of a Sherlock Holmes story.

CLIVE: I want to talk with you, Jill. I've got a lot of instructions to give you. (*The doorbell rings.*) That must be Bill now. Where can we talk in private?

JILL (*Rather bewildered*): In the kitchen, I suppose. Come on. (JILL *and* CLIVE *exit left. The doorbell rings again.* LYDIA *enters from left, humming her song. She goes to door and opens it.*)

LYDIA: Hello, Bill. (BILL BARNES *enters. He is a good-looking, serious-appearing youth of seventeen.*)

BILL: Hello, Lydia. Where is everybody?

LYDIA: Here and there, I guess. They'll be around before long. (BILL *comes down stage right to sofa and seats himself.* LYDIA *sits in chair at right of table.*) I'll keep you company till somebody comes down.

BILL: Where's Irene?

LYDIA: Upstairs dressing, I imagine.

BILL (*Sighing*): Gee, it must be wonderful to live in the same house with her!

LYDIA: Say, you've got it bad, haven't you! She's a bit older than you, you know.

BILL (*Very seriously*): That doesn't matter where there's true love. Besides, I'm very mature for my age.

LYDIA: I don't know about mature, but you certainly are a serious kid. Don't you ever think of going out and having a little fun? You're only young once, you know.

BILL (*Contemptuously*): Having fun! That's for kids and goons! I've got ambitions. I want to be a writer. I've got no time for kid stuff—parties, and goofy movies, and all that sort of thing. A writer has to live seriously; he has to see life as it really is.

LYDIA: By golly, you mean to tell me that writers don't believe in having a little fun?

BILL: That depends on what you call fun.

LYDIA: Fun's fun! It means enjoying yourself. To me it's fun to go to hear somebody like Terry Bromo sing. That boy does something to me; when he croons a low note, the shivers creep up and down my spine like little mice!

BILL: Shucks, I don't think Terry Bromo's so hot. He just sort of whimpers into a microphone like a dying calf.

LYDIA: What? Say, if that's an example of how a writer thinks, I'll keep away from books! Boy, you don't live; you just exist! (*She rises angrily to her feet.*) Sick calf, eh! Humph! (LYDIA *exits left angrily with a toss of her head.* BILL *remains seated, chuckling to himself; after a moment* JILL *enters from left. She is smiling and looks happier and more lively.*)

JILL: Hi, Bill. (BILL *rises to his feet politely.*)

BILL: Hello. (JILL *seats herself in chair which* LYDIA *has just vacated.*)

JILL: How are things at school? I haven't seen much of you, but I read your short story in the school magazine. It was very good.

BILL: Thanks. (BILL *seats himself.*)

JILL: Mr. Holm said in English class that he thought your story was one of the best pieces of student writing that he'd ever seen.

BILL (*Visibly pleased*): Gosh! Did he say that? He writes himself, you know.

JILL: Yes, I know. We've a book of his short stories there in the bookcase. (BILL *rises quickly from his chair, goes to bookcase, examines books rapidly, and takes one.*)

BILL: This is it! I've been trying to get a copy for a long time. (*Turns to* JILL) I didn't know you read much, Jill.

JILL: Oh, yes. I read a great deal. It's my hobby.

BILL (*Regarding her with new interest*): Is that so? Say, we'll have to talk some time about our favorite authors.

JILL: That'll be nice. (CLIVE *enters from left and comes to center.*)

CLIVE: Hello, Bill. How's the boy?

BILL (*Not very enthusiastically*): Hello, Clive. I'm O.K.

CLIVE: I saw your story in Jill's copy of the school magazine. Great stuff! Keep it up!

BILL: Thanks, Clive.

CLIVE: I've got to run down to the drugstore for some aspirin for Lydia. Tell Irene, when she comes down, that I'll be back soon, will you, Jill?

JILL: All right, Clive. (CLIVE *goes to door, then turns and looks meaningfully at* JILL.)

CLIVE: Carry on, Jill! (JILL *smiles and nods.* CLIVE *exits.* BILL *seats himself in chair at left of table.*)

JILL: You can borrow that book if you'd like to.

BILL: Thanks, I'd like to very much. (IRENE *suddenly enters at stairway right. As she descends the stairs, she raises her arms over her head and yawns widely. The change in her appearance must be very obvious. She is wearing an old, stained misfitting dress; her face is devoid of make-up and appears lined and sallow; her hair is wild and tangled. She looks very sleepy, and she rubs her eyes vigorously as she comes down to the sofa, on which she sinks with another wide yawn.* BILL *has risen to his feet and is staring at her—his mouth open in astonishment.* JILL *suppresses a giggle as she crosses to sofa and sits beside* IRENE. *The contrast between the two sisters as they sit side by side should be very striking.*)

IRENE: I've just had the nicest nap. I didn't know you were here, Bill, or I'd have made myself more presentable.

BILL (*Sinking into his chair with the air of a man having a bad dream*): Th—that's all right, Irene.

IRENE: I was so tired after dinner tonight, though. I've been dead tired for days. Getting old, I guess.

JILL (*Sweetly*): Is your rheumatism any better, Irene?

BILL (*In astonishment*): Rheumatism!

JILL: Yes, poor Irene suffers with it so much, especially in damp weather. Grandmother was the same way—before she died.

IRENE: The rheumatism is a little better. (*She rubs her side with a groan*) My teeth are bothering me again, though.

I suppose that one of these days I'll have to have them all out.

BILL: Gosh! That'll be terrible!

IRENE: Oh, it won't be so bad. Dentists make very clever false teeth nowadays. You can hardly tell them from the originals. Of course, sometimes they click like castanets when you're attacking a particularly tough piece of steak —but that's life!

BILL (*Shaking his head*): Yeah, I suppose so.

IRENE (*Yawning again*): It was nice of you to come over tonight, Bill.

BILL (*Uncomfortably*): I was just passing by, so I thought I'd drop in. (*He begins to rise from his chair*) I really ought to go. I—I've got to go over to the library and—

IRENE: Oh, sit down, Bill! What's the hurry? You've only just arrived.

JILL: Yes, don't go yet, Bill.

BILL: Well, I—

IRENE: Sit down, please. I'll wake up after a while. (BILL *seats himself reluctantly.*) Where's Clive?

JILL: He's gone down to the drugstore on an errand for Lydia. He'll be back soon.

IRENE: Oh, I hope he doesn't come back too soon! He wanted me to go to a movie tonight, but I just haven't strength enough to move out of here! Oh, to be your age again, Jill! (*During this dialogue,* BILL *is looking first at* JILL, *then at* IRENE, *impressed by the contrast between them as they sit together on the sofa.*)

JILL: Clive and I were just congratulating Bill on the wonderful story he had in the school magazine.

IRENE (*Yawning*): Story? Oh, did you write a story, Bill?

BILL: Why, yes, I did. I—

IRENE: Oh, well, I wouldn't know. I never read. When I

get home at night, all I'm good for is a nice long nap.

JILL: Mr. Holm thought the story was very good.

IRENE (*Indifferently*): That's nice. (*Sighing*) Jill, are there any more of those chocolates left? I know I shouldn't eat so many because they're ruining my teeth—but I just can't resist them!

JILL: I think there are still some in the box. (*Rising*) I'll get them. (JILL *exits left.* BILL *continues to sit and stare at* IRENE *in complete amazement.* IRENE *is now rubbing her eyes and yawning.*)

BILL: H—haven't you been feeling well, Irene?

IRENE: As well as can be expected, I guess. (JILL *enters with a box of chocolates. She comes to sofa, seats herself, and hands box to* IRENE, *who grasps it eagerly.* IRENE *reaches into the box, grabs several chocolates, and wolfishly stuffs them into her mouth.*)

IRENE (*With her mouth full*): Mmm—these are good! Just what the doctor ordered! (BILL *stares at her and shakes his head, a horrified expression on his face.*)

JILL: That's the last box, Irene. You ate the other two boxes of candy yesterday.

IRENE (*Chewing avidly*): Well, we'll just have to get some more. I've got to have chocolates!

JILL (*Smiling condescendingly*): Yes, I know. You've such a sweet tooth, Irene. (*The doorbell rings.*)

LYDIA (*From kitchen*): I'll get it! (*She enters from left, casts a look in* IRENE's *direction, and suppresses a shriek of delight. She goes to door and opens it.*) Well, it didn't take you long. (CLIVE *enters.*)

CLIVE: Your own brave knight has returned from his errand of mercy, fair lady.

LYDIA: Skip the fancy talk, and hand over the aspirin.

CLIVE: As you will, Queen Guinevere. (*He hands her a small package which she takes.* LYDIA *exits left.*)

CLIVE (*Coming to table at center*): Well, Irene, you're looking much better. Did you have a good rest?

BILL (*Bursting out involuntarily*): Better!

CLIVE: What's that, Bill?

BILL (*Swallowing*): Better. Yes, much better.

CLIVE: Yes, indeed! Irene looks more like her own beautiful self. Yesterday she was looking a bit tired.

IRENE: I imagine it's the energy in the chocolates, Clive. Candy always helps to revive me.

CLIVE: What you need is some nice fresh air; come on, and I'll take you for a little spin in the old jalopy.

IRENE: But, Clive, I'm so tired! (CLIVE *comes to sofa, takes* IRENE's *hands, and pulls her to her feet.*)

CLIVE: Now, none of that. Be a good girl, and do as Uncle Clive says.

IRENE (*Reluctantly*): Oh, all right. (IRENE *and* CLIVE *walk toward upper center door.* IRENE *limps very noticeably.*)

IRENE: That darned rheumatism!

CLIVE: Bad today?

IRENE: Terrible!

CLIVE: So long, kids. (CLIVE *and* IRENE *exit.* BILL *gazes after them, a bewildered expression on his features.* JILL *is smiling.* BILL *turns to look at her. He examines her steadily for a moment.*)

JILL: Cat got your tongue?

BILL: Gosh! Irene didn't look very well, did she?

JILL: Why, what do you mean, Bill? I thought she looked normal. After all, she had just awakened from a nap.

BILL: You mean she always looks like that right after she wakes up?

JILL: Of course! No woman is at her best at that time.

BILL: But, gosh—she looked—she looked so old!

JILL: Well, after all, she is getting on, you know. She's

twenty-two, and that's practically approaching middle age.

BILL: Yeah, I suppose so. But rheumatism! Gee, it's almost unbelievable.

JILL: She's had it for a long time now, poor thing.

BILL (*Rising to feet and examining* JILL *again with renewed interest*): That's a pretty dress you're wearing.

JILL: Why, thank you, Bill.

BILL: Say, I've got to go down to the library to get a book for a book report. Want to come along? We could go for a soda somewhere afterward.

JILL (*Rising*): I'd love to, Bill!

BILL: And—well—there's a dance next week at school. I'd like you to go with me.

JILL (*Smiling*): Wouldn't you rather take Irene?

BILL: With her rheumatism?

JILL (*Giggling*): Oh, I forgot—poor thing. Yes, I'd like to go, Bill; but now I'll have to tell Mother that we're going out. (*She goes to stairway right and calls*) Mother!

MRS. SAYERS (*From upstairs*): Yes, Jill.

JILL: I'm going for a walk with Bill.

MRS. SAYERS (*Surprised*): With whom?

JILL: With Bill—Bill Barnes!

MRS. SAYERS: Oh. All right, dear. Come home early.

JILL: I will. (*She smiles at* BILL, *and they exit, both looking very happy.* MRS. SAYERS *enters hurriedly at stairway, and comes to table.*)

MRS. SAYERS: Lydia! (LYDIA *enters from left.*)

LYDIA: Yes, ma'am.

MRS. SAYERS: Where are Irene and Clive?

LYDIA: I saw them go off in Clive's car.

MRS. SAYERS: Did you know that Jill has gone for a walk with that Barnes boy?

LYDIA: No, but I don't doubt it.

MRS. SAYERS: Just what has been going on around here, anyway? (*The doorbell rings.* LYDIA *goes to door and opens it.* IRENE *and* CLIVE *enter laughing excitedly.*)

MRS. SAYERS: Good heavens, Irene! You look like something out of a horror movie!

LYDIA: She's out of this world!

CLIVE: We can explain everything. (*He takes* MRS. SAYERS *by the arm, escorts her to the sofa, and gently seats her.*) We have a tale to tell, a tale of how young Bill Barnes was cured of his infatuation. Irene has been playing her old role as the Spirit of Poverty.

MRS. SAYERS: You mean that horrible part she once played in a school pageant?

IRENE (*Laughing*): Yes, and after my performance tonight, Helen Hayes and Katharine Cornell had better look to their laurels!

CLIVE: Yes, indeed! Nearly won the Academy Award!

LYDIA: It sure worked this time! Those two kids have gone off together.

CLIVE: I know. All we did was park the car around the corner and wait till they'd left.

MRS. SAYERS: Were you in on this, too, Lydia?

LYDIA: I sure was.

IRENE: We'll tell you all about it now, Mother. It was a scream!

LYDIA: It was out of this world!

MRS. SAYERS (*Shaking her head at* IRENE's *appearance*): For once I'm inclined to agree with you, Lydia. Out of this world, indeed! (*They all laugh as the curtains close.*)

THE END

Production Notes

OUT OF THIS WORLD

Characters: 2 male; 4 female.

Playing Time: 30 minutes.

Costumes: Everyday modern dress. Irene changes her costume during the play and appears in an old, stained, misfitting dress.

Properties: Dust cloth, box of chocolates, small package.

Setting: A modern American living room. There is a door up center which opens onto the front porch. There are windows at left and right of the door. At right is a stairway leading to rooms upstairs. At left is the door to the kitchen. In the center of the room is a table on which are several books and a vase of flowers. To right and left of the table are easy chairs. A sofa is downstage right, and another easy chair, downstage left. Against the wall at left is a well-filled bookcase.

Lighting: No special effects.

Stage Bore

Characters

MILLIE MILDEW, *a pretty girl of nineteen*
MRS. HAMMER, *proprietor of a theatrical boarding house*
HUNTER HAVAHART, *a veteran ham actor*
SALLY THESPIS, *an attractive young aspiring actress*
BILL BORDEN, *a young and breezy stage manager*
KATHERINE LEGRAND, *a famous, bad-tempered actress*
ZENOBIA, *her maid*

SCENE 1

TIME: *Late in the afternoon.*
SETTING: *The living room of Mrs. Hammer's boarding house in New York City.*
AT RISE: SALLY THESPIS *is standing before the sofa at center on which there is an open book.* MILLIE MILDEW *is seated in the armchair downstage left, watching* SALLY. SALLY *looks at the open book and reads aloud.*

SALLY: "A rose drinking the morning dew." (*She shakes her head.*) Golly, that's a tough one!
MILLIE (*Wryly*): You're not kidding.
SALLY: Anyway, here goes. (*She closes her eyes, smiles dreamily,*)

135

and with mouth half-open begins to breathe deeply. Her smile becomes a look of ecstasy as she breathes. She continues this for a moment or two.)

MILLIE: Great! Simply great! You make Helen Hayes look like an apprentice.

SALLY: I may not be Ethel Barrymore, but at least I'm trying. (*Looking down at book*) Let's see what's next.

MILLIE: I'll bet it's a lulu!

SALLY: It is. Listen to this. "A good exercise in revealing pantomime is to attempt to suggest a hungry woman— one who has not eaten in days—who is suddenly given a broiled sirloin steak."

MILLIE: I could do that one standing on my head. I haven't seen a sirloin steak since I left home in Podunk, Iowa.

SALLY: Here I go! (*She begins to stare wild-eyed at an imaginary steak. Her hands begin to tremble as she lifts imaginary knife and fork. Then she attacks the imaginary steak, cutting madly with the knife and wolfing each imaginary mouthful. Her mouth seems to be full, her cheeks are bulging when* MRS. HAMMER *rushes into the room.*)

MRS. HAMMER (*Watching* SALLY, *who has not yet seen her, while* MILLIE *giggles*): Why, Sally Thespis, what in the world are you doing?

SALLY (*Startled*): Oh, it's you, Mrs. Hammer. I'm just practicing. It certainly doesn't seem as though any of New York's producers think I'm the next great American actress, so about all I can do is practice.

MILLIE: Me, too. We want the stage, but the stage doesn't want us.

MRS. HAMMER: Don't be discouraged, Millie. And as for you, Sally, you've been here only a few months. Rome wasn't built in a day.

SALLY: That's what Professor Dramatesky says. He keeps

telling Millie and me to work at improving our technique. That's why we're using this book. The Professor says a great actress should be able to convey all emotions without saying a word. She should even be able to impersonate inanimate objects. (*Smiling*) Before I became a hungry woman, I was a rose drinking in the morning dew.

MILLIE: And what a rose! Any florist would love you!

MRS. HAMMER: Think of that! That's just wonderful! Of course, I was on the stage myself. Ah, the thrill of opening night! The flowers in the dressing room! The morning reviews! Have I ever shown you my scrapbook?

MILLIE (*Hurriedly*): About fifty times, Mrs. Hammer.

MRS. HAMMER: But that's all gone. All gone. (*Sadly, as she pats her ample figure*) I just never could keep away from sweets. Pounds and the acting profession don't mix. When I found I was fighting a losing battle with my appetite, I left the profession. So I did the next best thing; I opened a boarding house for actors.

SALLY: And we're glad you did. You've been wonderful to us.

MRS. HAMMER: Glad to help. I felt I owed it to the profession.

MILLIE: But things are looking up—at least for one of us. Sally has had the most wonderful break! Bill Borden took her down to Morley Miscue's office.

MRS. HAMMER: Morley Miscue, the great producer-director! Why, I know him. He refused me a part once—said he was afraid I might charge him for my services by the pound.

SALLY: Yes, it's the same Morley Miscue. He's looking for an understudy for Katherine LeGrand.

MRS. HAMMER: Katherine LeGrand! My! My! I heard she was doing a new play. "Bitter Brew," isn't it?

SALLY: Yes, and since Bill Borden is stage manager for the production, he thought he'd put in a word for me.

MILLIE: Bill's a peach.

MRS. HAMMER: And what did Morley Miscue say?

SALLY: He thinks I'd be all right for the job. But Katherine LeGrand has to approve of me first. She wasn't around when I was in Mr. Miscue's office.

MRS. HAMMER: Well, I certainly hope you get the job.

MILLIE: So do I. Sally's a really talented girl; I'll bet she's better right now than Katherine LeGrand.

MRS. HAMMER: Don't let Miss LeGrand hear you say that! She's supposed to have a terrible temper.

SALLY: Bill says she has the disposition of a cobra and a heart of steel to match. (HUNTER HAVAHART *enters at right*.)

HAVAHART (*In a hammy manner*): "Speak the speech, I pray you, as I pronounced it to you, trippingly on the tongue." Ah, how well the Bard expresses himself. (*Bowing*) Good afternoon, ladies.

MRS. HAMMER: Hello, Mr. Havahart.

SALLY: Hi, Hunter.

MILLIE: You look tired, Hunter.

HAVAHART (*Sinking into armchair, downstage right*): Ah, rest for the weary! I have had a trying day. To think that Hunter Havahart, who has tread the boards with John Barrymore, Sir Laurence Olivier, and Maurice Evans, would ever descend to reading a role on a radio soap opera. But one must eat.

SALLY: Be thankful you've got a job, Hunter.

MILLIE: Jobs are rare these days.

HAVAHART: I am thankful—in moderation. But how have the mighty fallen! (*Dramatically*) Let me not think on it!

Did I hear the name of that she-devil, Katherine Le-Grand, mentioned as I made my entrance?

MILLIE: Yes, Sally may be her understudy in "Bitter Brew."

HAVAHART (*To* SALLY): My child, my heart bleeds for you.

MRS. HAMMER: You know Miss LeGrand, Mr. Havahart?

HAVAHART: Know her? It is to laugh. Know her, indeed! Come here, Mrs. Hammer. (MRS. HAMMER *goes to him.*) Give me your hand. (*She does so.*) Now feel this. (*He guides her hand to his right temple.*)

MRS. HAMMER: You've got a scar there!

HAVAHART: Exactly. A souvenir of a production called "April Sunrise" in which I appeared with that 20th Century Lady Macbeth. She threw a lamp at me during rehearsal. Her aim was deadly. She could pitch for the Yankees tomorrow.

MRS. HAMMER: Goodness! She must have a real temper!

HAVAHART: Temper! That's an understatement. She once bit clean through my thumb. The wound required five stitches.

MILLIE: She sounds positively ghastly!

SALLY: Gosh, it looks as though I'm being thrown to the lions!

HAVAHART: My dear young ladies, you have no idea how ghastly she can really be. Strong men scream, and children whimper in terror whenever Katherine LeGrand appears on the scene.

MRS. HAMMER (*Practical*): She gets good parts, though.

HAVAHART: She does, indeed. I sometimes think it's because no producer would dare refuse her anything.

MILLIE: And to think that Sally may be mixed up with such a woman!

HAVAHART (*Philosophically*): Well, it's a job, anyway. And

perhaps no more dangerous than taming lions, or working in a dynamite factory. (BILL BORDEN *enters at right.*)

BILL: Hi, everybody. Boy, have I got news that is news.

SALLY (*Excitedly*): You mean I've got the job, Bill?

BILL: Well, maybe. It's still in the lap of the gods—or rather in the lap of Miss Katherine LeGrand, the toast of Broadway.

HAVAHART: And the terror of the plains!

BILL: You see, Sally, the reason the great Katherine wasn't on hand in Miscue's office when you were there is that she was being photographed for *Life* or *Look* or *Peep* or *Keyhole*—one of those picture magazines, anyway.

HAVAHART: Heaven help the photographers on a night like this!

BILL: Anyhow, here's my news. She's coming here, Sally— actually coming here in a few moments to interview you.

SALLY (*Overcome*): Oh! Need I say that I'm completely, absolutely, and positively terrified. Oh gosh, I hope she likes me.

HAVAHART (*Gloomily*): You're young. You're beautiful. You're charming. (*Pausing*) Consequently, she won't like you.

MRS. HAMMER: Mr. Havahart, don't be such a spoil-sport. You're just like a director I had once—

BILL: I'm sorry to cut into your reminiscences, Mrs. Hammer, but time's a-wasting. Anyway, I've done all I could. As stage manager for "Bitter Brew," I had the right to recommend Sally for the understudy's role. (*Sadly*) You may be right though, Hunter. The great LeGrand doesn't like pretty girls around her. Too much competition. (*Admiringly*) And Sally is certainly pretty.

SALLY: Thanks, Bill. You're nice, too.

HAVAHART: You see, Sally, if you looked like one of the

witches in "Macbeth" or like Madame Defarge on one of her bad days, the viper LeGrand might take you to her heart. (*He begins to recite in a shrill, sing-song voice.*) "When shall we three meet again? In thunder, lightning, or in rain?"

MRS. HAMMER: I don't see how anyone can help liking Sally. She's just like that lovely Beatrice Benifice I played with in—

SALLY (*Hurriedly interrupting*): Thanks, Mrs. Hammer. But, golly, you're all giving me goose pimples. If Miss Le-Grand doesn't hire me, I'm washed up. I've been in New York now for six months, and my money is just about gone. When Dad agreed to finance me here, he made me promise that if I hadn't made good in six months, I'd return home and get a job in an office.

MILLIE: A fate worse than death!

SALLY (*Sighing*): And I just don't want to work in an office —at least not in Loonville, Oklahoma.

HAVAHART (*Dramatically*): "All the world's a stage, and all the men and women merely players."

BILL (*Affectionately*): Now, Sally, don't give up hope. After all, I'm on your side, and Bill Borden is a mighty powerful colleague.

SALLY: Oh, Bill, you've been so nice.

BILL: Of course I have. That's my great charm. All over New York, people are constantly exclaiming, "Isn't that Bill Borden a prince of good fellows!" You hear it everywhere.

MILLIE (*Excitedly*): Sally, I've got a wonderful idea!

HAVAHART: Splendid! What is it?

MRS. HAMMER: Don't keep us in suspense, Millie.

MILLIE: Well, it may sound silly, but it's worth trying. You, Hunter, and you, Bill, seem to agree that Katherine

LeGrand is a mighty jealous female and that she just doesn't like pretty girls around her for fear they'd show her up. After all, she's no longer a chicken.

HAVAHART: Indeed, she isn't. She's as old as I am.

MRS. HAMMER: How old is that, Mr. Havahart?

HAVAHART (*Hesitantly*): Er- er- well, let's say, my dear Mrs. Hammer, that both Katherine LeGrand and I are beginning to be mature.

SALLY: What's your idea, Millie?

MILLIE: Well, gosh, if Miss LeGrand doesn't like pretty girls, why be pretty?

BILL (*Bewildered*): Come again. And in words of one syllable, please.

MILLIE: Why doesn't Sally just make herself as unattractive as possible? In fact, why doesn't she do a job on herself so she'll look like a regular frump? Then Miss LeGrand certainly won't think she'll have any competition.

HAVAHART: Ah, woman, woman! Thou wert fashioned to beguile!

MILLIE (*Eagerly*): Well, what do you think?

BILL: Now, wait a minute. (*He looks thoughtful.*) Do you know—the plan is so crazy it might work!

MRS. HAMMER: It might be worth trying.

HAVAHART: What you'll be doing, Sally, is playing on the ghastly LeGrand's greatest weakness, her insufferable conceit. If I know her—and I have the scars and bruises to prove I do—I think this plan might do the trick.

SALLY: Golly, I'm willing. And I think you're perfectly brilliant, Millie.

MILLIE: I guess it comes from being a flower and drinking in the morning dew. That's bound to strengthen your mind.

SALLY: By golly, I'll do it. What can I lose? I either get

the job, or I go home to Loonville and spend my days at a typewriter. Come on, Millie. You can help me ruin myself.

MILLIE: I'm right with you. (*Both girls go toward right exit.*)

BILL: Don't dilly-dally, though. Katherine LeGrand will be here at any moment.

SALLY: We'll hurry.

MILLIE: We promise. (*They exit excitedly.*)

HAVAHART: We shall shortly witness a performance that will make the opening night of *Hamlet* seem as flat as Katherine LeGrand's head. (*The phone rings.* MRS. HAMMER *answers it.*)

MRS. HAMMER: Hello. Oh, it's you, Molly. How are you? . . . Is that so? . . . Yes, of course, I know who it is. It's Katherine LeGrand. That's right—Katherine LeGrand . . . I'll bet she is . . . Well, of course I don't like to brag, but I do get the best people here. Yes, I'll tell you all about it when I see you . . . Goodbye, Molly. (*She hangs up and returns to center.*) That was Molly Jenkins across the street. She's all in a dither because a Cadillac with a chauffeur just parked in front of the house. There are two passengers—a beautifully dressed woman and another one not quite so well rigged out.

BILL: That's the great LeGrand all right. The other woman is Zenobia, her maid.

MRS. HAMMER: In that case, I'd better let them in. (*She exits right.*)

HAVAHART: Now for the fireworks. I haven't had so much fun since I played with the Marx Brothers!

BILL: I just hope it works.

HAVAHART: How can it fail? You know Katherine. If Sally ever appeared as her real self, LeGrand would take one look at her dewy freshness and bright, shining youth and make for the nearest door. But if Sally looks dowdy enough, she has a chance for the job.

BILL: Well, Sally's a good kid, and she certainly deserves a break.

HAVAHART: Ah, you have a soft spot in your heart for her, hey, my boy?

BILL: I sure have. She's tops. (Mrs. HAMMER *enters at right, followed by* KATHERINE LeGRAND *and* ZENOBIA.)

MRS. HAMMER: It's so nice to have you here, Miss LeGrand. You know Mr. Havahart and Mr. Borden, don't you?

KATHERINE: I know them well. How are you, Hunter? I heard you the other day on that horrible radio soap opera program. You sounded as smooth, suave, and completely unconvincing as a shaving cream commercial.

HAVAHART (*Bowing*): Ah, Katherine, I see that neither time nor tide has dulled the sharpness of your tongue.

KATHERINE: And hello, Bill. I didn't recognize you at first without a banana stuck in your mouth.

BILL: Hello, Katherine.

KATHERINE: And I wish you'd stop eating those bananas at rehearsal. Bananas give me the creeps. Their skins are so treacherous.

BILL: I'm sorry, Katherine. But I have to get a bite to eat when I can.

KATHERINE (*Imperiously*): Well, lay off bananas.

MRS. HAMMER: Won't you sit down, Miss LeGrand? (KATHERINE *looks around the room with ill-disguised distaste.* ZENOBIA *goes quickly to sofa, takes a handkerchief, and wipes off dust from the seat.*)

ZENOBIA: Sit here, Miss LeGrand.

KATHERINE (*Going to sofa and sitting*): Well, let's get down to business. Where's the young Helen Hayes?

BILL: Sally will be here in a moment.

KATHERINE: Actually, I need an understudy about as much as I need a hole in the head. I haven't missed a performance in years. When was the last time I was ill, Zenobia?

ZENOBIA: Gosh, Miss LeGrand, you're so seldom sick that it's hard to remember. I think you missed one performance of "Home Is the Sailor."

KATHERINE: That's right. I remember now. I had a slight cold.

HAVAHART: "Home Is the Sailor." (*Sarcastically*) That was years ago. Let's see—that must have been 19—

KATHERINE (*Hastily*): Never mind the year, Hunter.

HAVAHART: I was just trying to be helpful.

KATHERINE: Yes, about as helpful as a swamp snake. (MILLIE *suddenly enters at right.* KATHERINE *regards her rather hostilely.*) If this is the girl, I can tell you now she won't do.

HAVAHART (*Ironically*): She is attractive, isn't she, Katherine?

KATHERINE: She's just not the type. I can see that at once.

BILL: This isn't Sally Thespis, Katherine. It's Millie Mildew. She's a friend of Sally's.

MILLIE (*Laughing*): Bill's right. I'm not Sally. (SALLY *appears in right doorway.*) But here's Sally now. (SALLY *has donned glasses for the occasion. Her hair is rumpled, she is grinning rather moronically, and when she walks toward center, she turns her right toe in to give a crab-toed effect.*)

KATHERINE (*Visibly pleased*): So this is, Sally.

SALLY (*Curtseying awkwardly*): How do you do, Miss Le-Grand.

KATHERINE: Now this is more like it. We can probably use this girl.

SALLY (*Rapturously*): Oh, Miss LeGrand. You don't know how thrilling this is. I've heard so much about your kindness. (HAVAHART *smothers a laugh.*)

KATHERINE (*Melting*): Have you, my child? I'm not surprised. (*With a martyred air*) "So shines a good deed in a naughty world." (*More sharply*) Though sometimes all you get for a thoughtful attitude is a good swift kick in the pants.

SALLY: Oh, I'm sure that everyone appreciates your kindness, Miss LeGrand.

BILL: You can't make a mistake with Sally, Katherine. She even knows your role.

KATHERINE (*Suspiciously*): She what?

SALLY: You see, Miss LeGrand, whenever you are opening in a play, I try to learn your role. Then I go to see the production. In that way, I get an invaluable lesson in acting.

KATHERINE: Wise child! Wise child!

HAVAHART (*Aside*): In more ways than one.

KATHERINE: To give you the truth, child, you're not another Helen of Troy. But, after all, only a few of us in the theater have genuine beauty.

SALLY: I know that, Miss LeGrand. (*Scratching her side awkwardly*) But I promise to work hard.

KATHERINE: And don't kid yourself about what you'll be doing as my understudy. About all that will be required of you is to be on hand at each performance.

SALLY: All I ask is the chance to observe your technique.

KATHERINE: And, let me tell you, it's just about the best technique in the theater today.

HAVAHART (*Sarcastically*): Don't be such a shrinking violet, Katherine.

KATHERINE: Nuts to you, Hunter. And don't forget, Sally—
that is your name, isn't it—that your chances of getting
onto the stage during the run of "Bitter Brew" are practically nil. I'm as healthy as a horse. Isn't that right,
Zenobia?

ZENOBIA: Sure thing, Miss LeGrand.

HAVAHART (*Dramatically*): "A horse! A horse! My kingdom
for a horse!"

KATHERINE (*Dripping with sarcasm*): Hunter, you've got
enough ham in you to stock all the nation's meat coun-
ters. (*Rising*) Well, the thing's settled. (*To* BILL) You can
tell Morley that this kid will be okay. Although I still
say that I don't need an understudy.

SALLY: Oh, thank you, Miss LeGrand. (*She scratches her
side again awkwardly*)

KATHERINE: You got bugs or something?

SALLY: Oh, no, Miss LeGrand. It's just nerves, I guess.

HAVAHART (*Chuckling*): Or just plain nerve.

BILL (*Hastily*): Thanks for taking the trouble to come by,
Katherine.

KATHERINE: It *was* trouble. I should be at the hairdresser's
now. But if you really want to show appreciation, lay off
eating bananas on the set.

HAVAHART (*Singing*): "Yes, we have no bananas; we have
no bananas today."

KATHERINE: Don't ever try to get a part in a musical,
Hunter. With that voice, you'd set the theater back fifty
years.

HAVAHART: Thanks for the unsolicited advice.

KATHERINE: Come on, Zenobia. Time to go.

ZENOBIA: Yes, Miss LeGrand.

MRS. HAMMER: I'll show you out.

KATHERINE (*As she follows* MRS. HAMMER *toward right*): And remember, Bill—lay off those bananas, or I'll have your scalp.

BILL: Sure thing, Katherine. (KATHERINE *and* ZENOBIA *exit, following* MRS. HAMMER.)

MILLIE (*Embracing* SALLY): You did it! You were wonderful!

BILL (*Also embracing* SALLY): You ought to be given an Oscar!

SALLY: A job at last—and at real money. I won't have to go back to Loonville after all. Thanks, Millie, for your wonderful idea!

MILLIE (*Modestly*): It was nothing. I have them all the time.

HAVAHART: The years have been kind to Katherine. She hasn't lost a bit of her unlikeable personality.

BILL: Well, Sally has the job, anyway.

HAVAHART: Far be it from me to throw cold water on all this, but let's reserve our judgment. Katherine LeGrand wasn't born yesterday—not by any means. Let's just hope and pray that Sally isn't being thrown, as the Bard says, into "a sea of troubles." (*They all look thoughtful as the curtain closes.*)

CURTAIN

* * * *

SCENE 2

TIME: *About eight o'clock in the evening, a week later.*

SETTING: *Same as Scene 1.*

AT RISE: MRS. HAMMER *is sitting on sofa, leafing through a magazine.* HUNTER HAVAHART *is studying a script in armchair at downstage left.*

HAVAHART (*Reading aloud from script*): "My dear Ethel, I know that things have not been going well. First, the house burned down, then Grandma Merrieweather broke her leg, then Grandpa was arrested for shop-lifting, and now Cousin Hortense has lost her job in the glue factory. But Ethel, my dear, we must look on the bright side of things. Where there is life, there is hope. Behind each cloud there is a silver lining. For every desolate today, there is a bright tomorrow." (*He throws the script on the floor.*) Have you ever heard anything worse than this sugar-coated misery, Mrs. Hammer? Whoever writes these radio soap operas must be up to his neck in gloom and woe. And to think that I, Hunter Havahart, who have played the Bard from one end of the nation to the other, must stoop so low as to read such tripe over the air.

MRS. HAMMER: It's a job, anyway, Mr. Havahart.

HAVAHART (*Gloomily*): And what a job!

MRS. HAMMER: It's so nice that all my boarders are working. Even Millie did a TV commercial the other day.

HAVAHART: Good for her.

MRS. HAMMER: And "Bitter Brew" opens tonight. (*She looks at her watch.*) Just think of it, a half-hour from now, the curtain will rise. Ah, the wonder of opening night!

HAVAHART: And the ghastly Katherine LeGrand will be strutting her stuff. Tell me, has Sally been keeping out of the great LeGrand's way? Wasn't it wonderful the way Sally fooled her?

MRS. HAMMER: It was a tonic—a real tonic! Yes, Sally has been on hand at rehearsals all week—and she's been wearing the glasses and looking a mess. It's a shame that such a pretty girl has to masquerade like that.

HAVAHART: But as Shakespeare says, "Discretion is the better part of valor."

MRS. HAMMER: Tonight, though, Sally really looked beautiful before she left for the theater.

HAVAHART: You mean she didn't wear her witch's disguise?

MRS. HAMMER: No, she didn't—and I don't blame her. She said that an opening night is an opening night, after all. And she wanted to look her best.

HAVAHART: That's a dangerous business. (MILLIE MILDEW *enters right.*)

MILLIE: Hi, folks. Well, tonight's the night. And Katherine LeGrand is in the best of health. Sally looked lovely when she left for the theater.

HAVAHART: I hope she has sense enough to keep out of the great LeGrand's sight.

MILLIE: I hope so. (*The phone rings.*) Want me to get it, Mrs. Hammer?

MRS. HAMMER: Yes, go ahead, Millie. (MILLIE *goes to phone and lifts receiver.*)

MILLIE: Hello . . . Oh, it's you, Bill. How are things going? . . . What! . . . Oh, that's perfectly awful . . . She did? . . . Well, I'll bet Sally is in tears. I don't blame her. What a tough break! . . . Well, tell her to cheer up, anyway. We're all with her, no matter what has happened . . . Yes, I can guess. We all know what a poisonous tongue Miss LeGrand has when she really cuts loose . . . All right, Bill. I'm sorry things have turned out so horribly. 'Bye. (*She hangs up, looking desolate.*)

HAVAHART: What's wrong? You look like something in the last act of "Murder at Midnight."

MILLIE: Everything is wrong. Miss LeGrand saw Sally tonight—and Sally looked like a dream. So Miss LeGrand knew she had been fooled. She called Sally all the names in the book—

HAVAHART: And Katherine knows them all, I assure you.

MILLIE: And then she fired her on the spot. Poor Sally has been crying her eyes out.

MRS. HAMMER: Poor child!

HAVAHART: And yet I expected the worst when I heard Sally had dressed and preened herself for the occasion.

MILLIE: So I suppose it's back to Loonville for her.

HAVAHART (*Sadly*): A fate worse than death.

MILLIE: Oh, why can't things work out the way they should? Why do such things have to happen?

HAVAHART: My dear child, I've been asking myself those questions for years—and I never seem to hit on the answers.

MRS. HAMMER: That Miss LeGrand is certainly a hard-hearted woman.

HAVAHART: If Katherine has a heart, then I am, as the Bard says, "a sweet, unthinking babe!" (*The phone rings. MILLIE walks dejectedly to it and lifts receiver.*)

MILLIE (*Gloomily*): Hello . . . (*Perking up*) You again, Bill . . . What! . . . Oh, that's just too wonderful for words . . . But how did it happen? . . . (*Giggling*) You're kidding! . . . *Really?* . . . Oh, Bill, I just can't believe it! It's like a dream come true . . . You just bet we'll see you later. A real celebration is in order . . . Yes, I'll tell Mrs. Hammer and Hunter. They'll be delighted—and I'm thrilled beyond words . . . 'Bye. (*She comes excitedly to center.*) Guess what? You'll never believe it.

HAVAHART: From your radiant face, I suspect you're the bearer of good tidings.

MILLIE (*Dramatically*): Sally Thespis will play the lead in "Bitter Brew" tonight!

MRS. HAMMER: Oh, how thrilling! But what happened?

MILLIE: Katherine LeGrand has broken her ankle. She slipped on a banana peel.

HAVAHART: Three cheers for Bill Borden and his bananas!

MILLIE: So there wasn't anything anybody could do. Sally just has to go on in the part. What a break for her! And she'll be able to do the role for weeks!

HAVAHART: Do you suppose that if we went over to the theater we could get seats? We'll be a little late, but it's worth trying.

MILLIE: I'd certainly love to see Sally in action!

MRS. HAMMER: And so would I.

HAVAHART: Then what are we waiting for? Ladies, you will be my guests at the unveiling of a new Broadway star.

MILLIE: Oh, thank you, Hunter.

MRS. HAMMER: Thanks, Mr. Havahart.

HAVAHART: Don't mention it. After all, my ill-gotten gains from soap opera ought to be put to good use. On to "Bitter Brew." (*They all exit right excitedly as the curtains close.*)

CURTAIN

* * * *

SCENE 3

TIME: *Early the following morning.*

SETTING: *The same. There are several vases of flowers all over the room.*

AT RISE: SALLY *and* BILL *are sitting side by side on the sofa.* BILL *is studying the morning papers carefully for reviews of* "Bitter Brew." MILLIE *stands by sofa.* HAVAHART *is seated in armchair at downstage left;* MRS. HAMMER *sits in armchair at downstage right.*

SALLY: Gosh, you'll never know how I felt last night. Talk about butterflies in your stomach. I must have had a million of them! And when I first walked out onto the stage, my knees were shaking like a pair of castanets.

HAVAHART: But you did beautifully, my child.

MRS. HAMMER: You brought the tears to my eyes.

MILLIE: And to mine, too.

BILL: Listen to what Perly Gates says in the *Chronicle*. "A shining new star was born last night to join the galaxy of Broadway greats. A refreshing talent, Miss Sally Thespis, understudy to Katherine LeGrand, caught the hearts and minds of the capacity audience in a radiant and perceptive performance that rated the cheers it received."

MILLIE: Oh, Sally, isn't that just wonderful!

BILL: And that isn't all, friends. That isn't all. Now hear this! Here's what Gilbert Foghorn says in the *Daily Echo:* "An enthusiastic Broadway audience was treated last night to one of the most auspicious stage debuts in our memory. The newcomer was slim, attractive, bubbling Sally Thespis, who is obviously on the threshold of what should be one of the most glitteringly successful careers in theater annals."

MILLIE: You just bowled them over, Sally!

SALLY: I still can't believe it. And just look at these flowers!

BILL: Yep. And it's all here in black and white.

SALLY (*Kissing him impetuously on the cheek*): Gosh, everyone is so nice!

BILL: Well, thanks. If this is what happens, I only wish you'd have a Broadway opening every night.

SALLY: But my conscience really is bothering me. It just doesn't sound fair. Here I am with success on my hands, and poor Katherine LeGrand is flat on her back. I can't help feeling sorry for her.

HAVAHART: My dear Sally, don't waste your charming sympathy. If anyone can weather the "slings and arrows of outrageous fortune," it's Katherine LeGrand.

BILL (*Smiling knowingly*): It was just Fate, that's all. She was just coming from her dressing room and was crossing over to Harley Simpson's dressing room when she fell on the banana peel. (*The phone rings.*)

HAVAHART: Don't disturb yourselves. I'll answer it. (*He goes to phone and lifts receiver.*) Hello . . . Why, Katherine, my dear, need I say that I was positively shaken to the very core when I heard of your unfortunate accident. . . . Why, Katherine! What language! I never knew there were such words. . . . Yes . . . Oh, you'll be indisposed for at least six weeks. Isn't that sad! (*He waves his arms in silent hurrah to the others, who look joyful.*) Katherine, I am genuinely sorry—my cup of grief runneth over. (*He goes through pantomime of laughing heartily and continues to lead the silent hurrahs of the others.*) Well, Katherine, always remember, Hunter Havahart's kindest thoughts are with you always . . . Why, Katherine! (*He holds receiver away from his ears.*) Such language! . . . Goodbye, my sweet. (*He hangs up.*) My dear Sally, you have at least six weeks to shine!

MILLIE: Hurray!

MRS. HAMMER: We ought to celebrate now. There's all that food that we bought waiting in the kitchen. Mr. Havahart and Millie, why don't you help me bring it out? (*Joyfully*) This is just like old times. Ah, the theater! The theater!

HAVAHART: Lead on, Mrs. Hammer!

MILLIE: We're right with you. (MRS. HAMMER, MILLIE, *and* HAVAHART *exit right.* SALLY *and* BILL *come to center.*)

SALLY: Bill, this is all just unbelievable. Imagine it! Me, Sally Thespis, a star! I keep pinching myself to make sure I'm really here and that all this has actually happened to me.

BILL: You deserve every bit of it, Sally. (*Earnestly*) There's one thing I've been wanting to say, though. I know very well that from now on, our paths won't cross very often. You'll be traveling in a different world. You'll be in the big time and the bright lights of Broadway will be shining on you.

SALLY: What are you saying, Bill? Why, you made all this possible. You had faith in me, and you arranged the interview, and, oh, lots more.

BILL: But I don't want to be a millstone around your neck. After all, I'm just a stage manager. There's not likely to be a place for me in the glamorous life you'll be leading. And I want you to know, you mustn't feel you owe me anything. I don't want to stand in your way.

SALLY: Please, Bill—I've never heard anything so silly. I'm still Sally Thespis, remember? A Loonville, Oklahoma girl. Nothing will ever change that. And I won't let it. (*Affectionately*) Bill, I'll always want you around—forever and ever—but on one condition.

BILL (*Ecstatically*): And that is—

SALLY (*Grinning*): That you promise to eat bananas at the right time *from now on*.

BILL: It's a promise. (*They embrace just as* MILLIE, MRS. HAMMER, *and* HAVAHART *enter right, carrying various plates of food.*)

MILLIE: Bravo!

MRS. HAMMER: Isn't that romantic!

HAVAHART (*Dramatically*): Ah, what is it that the Bard says. Ha! I have it. "Seal with a kiss love's dateless bargain."

BILL: Okay. If you say so, Hunter. (*He kisses* SALLY.)

HAVAHART: Splendid. And now, if I may again quote the Bard, "Shall we set about some revels?" (*All laugh gaily and ad lib agreement as the curtains close.*)

THE END

Production Notes

STAGE BORE

Characters: 2 male; 5 female.

Playing Time: 35 minutes.

Costumes: Millie Mildew wears an attractive sweater and skirt. Mrs. Hammer wears a cotton housedress and apron. Hunter Havahart wears a velvet jacket and ascot. Sally Thespis might wear an attractive dark dress brightened with such accessories as a scarf, belt, and jewelry, which she removes when masquerading for Katherine LeGrand, leaving the dress plain. Bill Borden wears sports jacket and slacks. Katherine LeGrand wears a fashionable suit trimmed with a fur piece, if possible, and a stylish hat; she carries handbag and gloves. Zenobia is dressed in dowdy clothes.

Properties: Book, pair of glasses for Sally; telephone; handkerchief for Zenobia; script for Hunter Havahart; magazines for Mrs. Hammer; several newspapers for Bill Borden; various plates of food; several vases of flowers for Scene 3.

Setting: The living room of Mrs. Hammer's boarding house in New York City. The room is shabbily furnished. There is a battered sofa at center of stage. At left of sofa is a small end table with lamp on it. At downstage left and right are old armchairs. At upstage center is a table which holds a telephone and some magazines. On the walls of the room are several old theater posters, announcing:

157

"JOSEPH JEFFERSON IN RIP VAN WINKLE," "JOHN BARRYMORE IN HAMLET," "WALTER HAMPDEN IN CYRANO DE BERGERAC." On the upstage wall at center is a framed motto which says: "ALL THE WORLD'S A STAGE." There is an exit at right.

Lighting: No special effects.

The Natives Are Restless Tonight

Characters

LAUNCELOT FIG-NEWTON, *a stuffy Englishman of middle age*
MRS. FIG-NEWTON
HERMIONE FIG-NEWTON, *a pretty girl of twenty*
BRIAN BROADBOW, *a handsome young hunting guide*
GREGORY GOGGLE, *a veteran trader*
DR. AMANDA STRAITLACE, *a good-natured physician*
BONGO, *a native*
TONGO, *an educated native*
CROMO, *a native emissary from the Marilyn Mau-Mau tribe*
FOUR NATIVES

SETTING: *A camp in a jungle clearing, the headquarters of Launcelot Fig-Newton and his hunting party.*
AT RISE: LAUNCELOT FIG-NEWTON *and* BRIAN BROADBOW, *although dressed in shorts, knee-length socks and sun helmets, are definitely feeling the heat.*

FIG-NEWTON (*Mopping face with handkerchief*): Beastly hot, eh what, Brian? Beastly hot. Reminds me of India just before the monsoon season.

BRIAN: Africa has never been noted for its air-conditioning, Mr. Fig-Newton. And this is the very heart of the jungle.

(*Looks right and left nervously.*) In fact, not many Englishmen have been so deep in Africa as we are right now.

FIG-NEWTON (*Scratching his leg*): Makes one feel like a jolly
old pioneer, what? Trail-blazing and all that sort of
thing. (*Loudly, cupping hands to mouth.*) Hi-Ho, Sterling
Silver!

BRIAN: That's a hunting cry I've never heard.

FIG-NEWTON: The Americans use it, I believe. It's a sort of
password of one of their famous Western characters—the
Solitary Ranger, I think he's called.

BRIAN: Indeed! (*Shaking head*) Amazing people, Americans.
(*The beat of native drums is now heard offstage.*)

FIG-NEWTON: Gad, (*adjusting helmet*) there go those deucedly
infuriating drums again! (*Peers to right and left.*)

BRIAN (*Looking rather worried*): Yes, the natives are restless
tonight. There's something queer afoot. (*Looks to right
and left*) They seem to be furtive and not at all friendly.
As a guide with the welfare of his hunting party at heart,
I wonder if I have done right in bringing you and your
family to the innermost recesses of the African continent.

FIG-NEWTON: Think nothing of it, old boy. (*Slaps* BRIAN)
The Fig-Newtons have nerves of steel and iron constitu-
tions.

BRIAN: But your daughter, Hermione, is such a lovely and
fragile creature.

FIG-NEWTON (*Again scratching legs*): Blast these bugs! Lovely,
yes—Hermione, not the bugs. Fragile, perhaps. But she's
a Fig-Newton, Brian. Her ancestors have stood their
ground since the Battle of Hastings.

BRIAN: And there's your wife, too. After all, this is hardly
the life for a woman of her years.

FIG-NEWTON: Oh, come now, Brian. Don't worry about
Elizabeth. Her family goes back to St. George and I must

say she's got plenty of the Dragon in her. In any event, old bean, we're here to bag a lion, and I *must* have a lion. Boyhood dream, you know. Shot a tiger once back in India in '34, but must have a lion. (*Adjusts helmet*) Man's not lived until he's shot the king of beasts. Must jolly well do it, you know. (*Slaps* BRIAN *on back.*)

BRIAN (*Dramatically*): Come the dawn—and we shall set out.

FIG-NEWTON: Jolly good. Looking forward to it no end. (*The drums are beating more loudly*) Blast those drums. (*Looks to right and left*) Nerve-wracking, what? (*Four* NATIVES *with bright yellow hair, enter in single file. The leader of the line, a tall fellow, wears a white chef's hat. The two behind him look straight ahead, dead-pan. The last one in line, a little fellow with a wide grin, carries a bucket. The four stop at center, still in single file.*)

LEADER (*Pointing to bucket*): Bwana! Boona!

SMALL NATIVE (*Grinning*): Yum! Yum! (*He rolls his eyes at the bucket, and the* NATIVES *go forward and exit left.*)

FIG-NEWTON (*Looking after them, puzzled*): Oh, I say now, what in the world was all that fuss?

BRIAN: Mysterious, to say the least.

FIG-NEWTON: Most extraordinary-looking chaps! Blonde hair and all that. Most unusual!

BRIAN (*Shrugs*): These are perfect specimens of the Marilyn Mau-Mau tribe. No one knows where they originally came from. Pretty handsome, eh?

FIG-NEWTON (*Shudders*): These deuced natives are cannibals, aren't they? I hope I look as unappetizing to the Marilyn Mau-Maus as they look to me.

BRIAN: They *used* to be cannibals. (*Bites fingernails*)

FIG-NEWTON: Then, in that bucket, there might have been a tender piece of—

BRIAN: I didn't see any meat in it. Just some watery substance—only thicker.

FIG-NEWTON: *Blood* is thicker than water! (*He salutes, then stops, horrified.*) As the French say, it makes one furiously to think. (*Strikes forehead dramatically.* HERMIONE FIG-NEWTON *enters at left. She is dressed in a white skirt and blouse, heavy walking shoes and a sun helmet. When she enters,* BRIAN *removes his helmet.*)

HERMIONE: There's something positively ghastly about those drums! (*Folds arms. Stands with feet wide apart.*) And they go on and on. (*To* BRIAN) Please put on your helmet, Brian. You'll get a ghastly sunstroke.

BRIAN: A man worth his salt should acknowledge the presence of beauty. (*Bows ceremoniously*)

HERMIONE: Oh, Brian, (*Titters*) you do say the nicest things.

FIG-NEWTON: Where's Mother, Hermione?

HERMIONE: She's resting in the tent before dinner. Those hideous drums have given her a miserable headache.

BRIAN: I sympathize with her. (*Bows again.*)

HERMIONE (*Worried*): Just what do the drums mean, Brian? Do they bode trouble of some kind?

FIG-NEWTON (*Intoning*): The natives are restless tonight.

BRIAN: One never knows about Africa. It's deep and mysterious. But something may be afoot. (*Looks right and left*) I was talking with Gregory Goggle this morning—

HERMIONE: You mean that funny little man who trades with the natives?

BRIAN: He may be a funny little man, but he's been around Africa for years. He knows the place. And he thinks something is up. (*Looks right and left*)

HERMIONE: Oh, how terrible! (*Wrings hands*)

FIG-NEWTON: Trouble or no trouble, the inner man must be fed. (*Slaps stomach*) I'm going to dress for dinner.

HERMIONE: Father, are you actually going to get into evening clothes just to dine in the midst of this awful jungle?

FIG-NEWTON: Indeed, I am! Always dressed for dinner all my life and don't intend to stop now. Where I go, the British Empire, God bless it, goes, too. (*Salutes*)

BRIAN (*Again removing helmet*): God save the Queen!

HERMIONE (*Warningly*): Sunstroke, Brian!

FIG-NEWTON: Anyone who's not willing to get a touch of the sun for the Queen is not a man. England expects every man to do his duty. (*Going toward right*) Cheerio! (*He exits.*)

HERMIONE: Father will never change. (*The drums beat loudly for a moment and then cease.*) Thank heaven the drums have stopped. (*Her right hand is at her heart, her left at forehead.*) They were becoming unbearable.

BRIAN: You're not to worry, Hermione. If anything should go amiss, I am here to protect you. (*Extends his hands to her*)

HERMIONE: Oh, Brian, you're so strong and manly. (*She takes his hand, and he puts his other arm around her.*)

BRIAN: The man does not live who would not willingly give his life for you, Hermione. (GREGORY GOGGLE *and* DR. AMANDA STRAITLACE *enter at left.* GOGGLE *is a short man dressed in shorts, a rather dirty shirt, and, incongruously, a black derby. His companion is a plump, bristling woman who speaks raucously and exudes good humor. She is carrying a doctor's black bag.*)

GOGGLE (*Speaks in slightly cockney accent, drops "h's"*): Whoops—didn't mean to break in on love's young dream.

BRIAN (*Dropping* HERMIONE's *hand*): Hello, Dr. Straitlace. Hello, Gregory.

AMANDA: Keep right at it, kids. What Africa needs is more

young lovers and fewer old traders like Gregory Goggle here. (*Digs him with her elbow*)

GOGGLE (*Shaking finger at her*): Now, Dr. Straitlace, you 'aven't a call to say that. You know you love me.

AMANDA: Goggle, you've got the sort of face only a near-sighted mother could love.

BRIAN: Excuse me, may I present Hermione Fig-Newton?

GOGGLE (*Eyeing her appreciatively*): I've seen the beautiful Miss Fig-Newton before, and 'ow could I forget 'er? (AMANDA *cracks* GOGGLE *good-naturedly but firmly on the back. He doubles up and coughs spasmodically after the blow.*)

AMANDA: Goggle, you old baboon, you've got the soul of a poet and the face of a pick-pocket. Anyway, Miss Fig-Newton, let me introduce myself. I'm Dr. Amanda Strait-lace, the medical profession's gift to Africa. I was sent out here by the African Medical Society to work among the Marilyn Mau-Mau tribe.

HERMIONE (*Holding out her hand*): How do you do? (*They shake hands, and* HERMIONE *winces at* AMANDA'S *iron grip.* AMANDA *looks into* HERMIONE'S *eyes, feels her forehead, and examines her skin.*)

AMANDA: Had any chills lately? Got any bumps on you—bumps that look like warts? Has your skin been cracking between the fingers?

HERMIONE: Heavens, no! (*Examining her fingers*)

AMANDA: Good! Then you probably haven't got African-isitis. It's the disease I find most among the Marilyn Mau-Maus.

HERMIONE: The Marilyn Mau-Maus? Aren't they the natives who beat the drums?

GOGGLE: You bet they are! They beat the drums to beat the band. There's trouble brewin' 'ere for sure. (*Gestures to indicate "this very spot"*) That tribe is in a stew about something, I can tell you.

BRIAN (*Gulping*): *Who's* in the stew?

AMANDA (*Intoning*): The natives are restless tonight. I don't know them too well, though. (*Begins to stir around in her bag, looking up from time to time*) Been here only a couple of days. Came down the river on one of those awful flat-bottomed boats. It wasn't exactly the kind of trip you read about in the travel folders.

GOGGLE: I'm 'ere to warn all of you. (*He removes his derby and mops his brow.*) What's 'appened is this. These bloomin' Marilyn Mau-Maus 'ave an idol in the village. It's a wooden image that's been 'anded down for generations. It's disappeared! Gone! So the Marilyn Mau-Maus are very upset. And when anything out of the way 'appens, the natives begin to suspect strangers. (*Gives each a quick look.*) And all of us are strangers—except maybe me. I've been tradin' with 'em for years.

AMANDA: I don't like the way some of them have been eyeing me, I can tell you. The village chief is about seven feet tall, and he has muscles (*Builds up muscles on left arm with right hand*) on his muscles.

GOGGLE: Yes, the Marilyn Mau-Maus run to bloomin' large sizes.

AMANDA: Large! That's a laugh. (*Opens bag; pulls out instruments as she talks.*) I lanced a boil on a fellow's neck yesterday, and I had to stand on a ladder to do it. (*Pause*) And he was the baby of the family.

BRIAN: You think then, Gregory, that there may be trouble? (*Quick look right and left*)

GOGGLE: I've been around Africa long enough to know when things go wrong. And the bloomin' Marilyn Mau-

Maus are obviously gettin' more worked up every minute. (*The four* NATIVES *again enter in single file from left led by the tall fellow in the chef's hat, with the little fellow carrying the bucket bringing up the rear. Leader stops at center.*)

LEADER: Bwana! Boona!

GOGGLE: Samaga! Boona!

SMALL NATIVE: Yum! Yum! (*The small* NATIVE *rolls his eyes at bucket, and the four exit, single file, right.*)

AMANDA: What's that (*Looking after them*)—the Hit Parade?

GOGGLE: Those are the Bandagwanda. They are specially selected by the tribe to test recipes. (*Smacks lips*)

HERMIONE: Recipes?

BRIAN: The Marilyn Mau-Maus used to be cannibals, didn't they?

GOGGLE: What do you mean used to be? The bloomin' fellows still have a taste for long pig.

AMANDA: I'd give a bit to know what is in that bucket.

GOGGLE: Take my advice, and don't investigate. What you don't know won't hurt you.

HERMIONE: Brian, (*Takes his arm*) after what Mr. Goggle has told us about the disappearance of the idol and the natives' unrest, don't you think we ought to give up this whole idea of hunting tomorrow? Why don't we just pack up and get away from here? (FIG-NEWTON *and his wife enter on last speech.* FIG-NEWTON *is now in his formal evening attire, and* MRS. FIG-NEWTON *is wearing an evening dress.*)

AMANDA: Say, I didn't know there was a fancy dress ball afoot. What is it—the Marilyn Mau-Mau Junior Prom?

FIG-NEWTON: What's all this about not going hunting tomorrow? Shame on you, Hermione. Shame. No Fig-Newton should let himself be frightened by a group of beastly natives. What have you been telling her, Goggle?

GOGGLE: The bloomin' truth, that's what. My advice to you is to 'ead for civilization as quickly as possible. (*All look right and left.*)

FIG-NEWTON: Nonsense. Won't hear of it. Came here to bag a lion. Intend to do so. The British Empire wasn't founded by people who ran for civilization at the slightest inconvenience.

MRS. FIG-NEWTON (*Slapping at her arm*): Bugs! Insects! I feel like a portable blood bank for mosquitoes.

AMANDA: I'm Dr. Amanda Straitlace. (*She shakes hands with the FIG-NEWTONS, who both wince at her grip.*) You two aren't exactly dressed either for the bugs or the climate, you know.

MRS. FIG-NEWTON (*Surprised*): But, my dear Dr. Straitlace, we always dress for dinner. Doesn't everyone?

FIG-NEWTON: Have to keep up appearances, don't you know? Don't have to be savages just because we're in the jungle. (AMANDA *cracks him on the back, and he doubles up and coughs.*)

AMANDA: There speaks the good old British Empire. I'm all for you, Mr. Fig-Newton. And about those bugs, Mrs. Fig-Newton (MRS. FIG-NEWTON *slaps at herself on neck*), I've got something here that might help. (*She opens her bag and takes out a tube of ointment.*) Just rub some of this on when you get time. It'll make you smell like a glue factory, but it'll keep the bugs away.

MRS. FIG-NEWTON: Thank you. Anything is preferable to being eaten alive.

HERMIONE: Speaking of being eaten alive, Mother, do you know that the Marilyn Mau-Maus are cannibals?

MRS. FIG-NEWTON: How terrible! (*Shivers*)

GOGGLE: I repeat, that's why it's best for you to give up your bloomin' safari, Mr. Fig-Newton.

BRIAN: Goggle knows the Marilyn Mau-Maus.

FIG-NEWTON: But he doesn't know us Fig-Newtons. No Fig-Newton ever turned his back on danger.

AMANDA (*Slapping him on the back again with same results*): You tell him, Mr. Fig-Newton. Long live the Queen!

FIG-NEWTON (*Snapping to attention*): The Queen, bless her!

GOGGLE: Well, you can't say I 'aven't warned you. And I tell you the natives regard the disappearance of Beegin-Beegeen as a bloomin' serious affair.

HERMIONE: Beegin-Beegeen?

GOGGLE: That's the name of the bloomin' idol. Which reminds me of an amusin' story Joe Graspy, another trader, told me. Seems that Joe visited the Marilyn Mau-Mau tribe and was shown the idol, Beegin-Beegeen. Can you guess what Joe said to the native chief?

AMANDA: I'll bet it was a lulu.

GOGGLE (*Chuckling*): He said, "Why, chief, I've heard about your idol all my life. We 'ave a popular song in my country about it. It's called 'Begin the Beguine.'" (*All laugh, except* FIG-NEWTON.)

FIG-NEWTON: Frankly, old man, I don't get it. Sorry and all that sort of thing—but it just doesn't register. (*Taps forehead*)

HERMIONE (*Soothingly*): No reason why it should, Father. It's an *American* joke. (*The drums begin beating once more.*)

MRS. FIG-NEWTON: Oh, no, (*Puts fingers in ears*) not those again!

AMANDA (*Looking into* MRS. FIG-NEWTON'S *eyes, feeling her forehead, and examining her skin*): Had any chills lately? Got any bumps on you? Has your skin been cracking between the fingers? (*Feeling* MRS. FIG-NEWTON'S *arm*) Ah, here's a bump.

MRS. FIG-NEWTON: That is merely a mosquito bite.

AMANDA: Good! Then you haven't got Africanisitis.

GOGGLE: I don't like those bloomin' drums. (*Looks right and left*)

AMANDA: Well, I've got to be returning to the village. (*Snaps bag shut*)

MRS. FIG-NEWTON: You mean you're actually going back when the natives are in such a strange mood?

AMANDA: It's my job, Mrs. Fig-Newton. We Straitlaces have our code, too. (*Nods righteously*)

FIG-NEWTON (*Pitching voice high*): Well said, madam, well said.

AMANDA (*Slapping his back*): I knew you'd approve.

MRS. FIG-NEWTON: You're both welcome to stay to dinner.

AMANDA: No. Thanks just the same. Have to be moving on. Some of my muscular friends may have indigestion.

GOGGLE: I 'ave to be gettin' a move on, too. (FIG-NEWTON *claps his hands twice.*)

FIG-NEWTON: Time for the native boys to begin serving the meal. (*Two natives,* BONGO *and* TONGO *enter at left.*) Start serving the soup.

BONGO (*Smiling*): Can do.

AMANDA: Just a moment. (*She goes to natives*) Which is which now?

BONGO: Me Bongo. Him Tongo.

AMANDA: Fine. Now listen, Bongo. You sabbee drums? (*She makes a motion of beating drums.*)

BONGO (*Grinning broadly*): Sure. Me sabbee. Drums. (*He goes through motions, too.*)

AMANDA: Great. Now we're getting somewhere. Be a good fellow now, and try to understand. Sabbee reason for drums?

BONGO (*Shrugging*): Kamana woggo chaga.

AMANDA: Come again.

GOGGLE: 'E says 'e doesn't understand.

AMANDA: No sabbee?

BONGO: No sabbee.

AMANDA (*Sighing*): Oh, well, you can't blame me for trying.

TONGO (*Who has been silent, suddenly speaking in rich Oxonian accents*): My dear madam, if you wish to be enlightened concerning the rather drab monotony of the drum beating, perhaps I might be of some assistance.

AMANDA: Great heavens! Who is this—Winston Churchill?

BRIAN (*Laughing*): I think I can explain. You see, Tongo happens to be a graduate of Oxford.

AMANDA: Why didn't you tell me?

GOGGLE: You didn't do any bloomin' askin'.

TONGO: I completely understand your consternation, madam. However, I have been Brian Broadbow's friend since our Oxford days. I owe him a great debt of gratitude.

BRIAN: Oh, come now, Tongo, it was nothing.

TONGO: It was a great deal! My friend, Brian Broadbow, once saved my life. At the risk of his own life, Brian stepped between me and a charging lion and shot the animal between the eyes.

BONGO: Plenty brave.

AMANDA: You said a mouthful, Bongo, old boy.

HERMIONE: Oh, Brian—how like you!

BRIAN (*Modestly*): It was nothing really.

FIG-NEWTON: Only what any true Englishman would do under similar circumstances.

TONGO: So when Brian agreed to lead Mr. Fig-Newton's hunting party, I was delighted to come along to help. It has afforded me an excellent opportunity, too, to visit with my people.

GOGGLE: You mean you've been in the village?

TONGO: Naturally, my dear fellow. I have four aunts, four uncles, thirty-two cousins, and countless friends there.

FIG-NEWTON: All this is jolly interesting and all that, but it's time to eat.

TONGO: We shall serve at once, sir.

BONGO (*Rubbing stomach*): Plenty food.

GOGGLE: Before you go, Tongo—don't you think all of us are in danger?

TONGO: I do indeed, sir. My people are extremely agitated by the disappearance of Beegin-Beegeen. I should not care to predict the consequences.

AMANDA: That's comforting.

BONGO: Plenty trouble.

AMANDA: O.K., little Sir Echo. We get the idea.

FIG-NEWTON: You may start bringing in the soup.

TONGO: At once, sir.

BONGO: Plenty fast. (TONGO *and* BONGO *exit right*.)

GOGGLE: I'll be goin' along with Dr. Straitlace. But you're makin' a bloomin' big mistake goin' on with that hunt tomorrow.

FIG-NEWTON: Decent of you to worry, old bean, but we Fig-Newtons can take care of ourselves.

AMANDA: See you later then—I hope.

MRS. FIG-NEWTON: Thank you for the ointment. (*Begins to put some on her arms.*)

AMANDA: Glad to have been of service. Ta! Ta! (*Exits*)

HERMIONE (*In a quivering voice*): I'm really frightened. Even Tongo seems to think we are in peril. (TONGO *and* BONGO *enter carrying bowls of soup which they put at each place.*)

FIG-NEWTON: Mmm. Smells delightful!

MRS. FIG-NEWTON (*Sarcastically*): Yes, there's nothing like a bowl of *hot, steaming* soup in the *hot, steaming* jungle.

HERMIONE: Well, let's make the best of it. (*They begin to eat.*)

FIG-NEWTON (*Suddenly beginning to laugh uproariously*): I have it! Oh, jolly good! Jolly good!

BRIAN: What is it, sir?

FIG-NEWTON (*Unable to control laughter*): Oh, I say, jolly good! Jolly good! "Begin the Beguine." Oh, I say, that *is* a smasher! (*He continues to laugh as the four* NATIVES *enter in single file as usual and led by the tall fellow in the white chef's hat. Leader stops at center and looks in bewilderment at* FIG-NEWTON, *evidently unable to understand* FIG-NEWTON's *loud laughter.*)

LEADER: Bwana! Boona!

SMALL NATIVE: Yum! Yum! (*They exit left.* FIG-NEWTON *continues to laugh, and the drums begin to beat again in a rising crescendo as the curtains close.*)

* * * *

SCENE 2

TIME: *Early next morning.*

SETTING: *Same as Scene 1.*

AT RISE: *No one is on stage. After a moment,* DR. STRAITLACE, *carrying her black bag, enters at right and comes to center. Suddenly,* BONGO, *obviously excited, rushes in from left.*

BONGO: Miss gone! Miss gone! (*He tries to rush by* AMANDA, *who grabs his arm in her vise-like grip. He winces.*)

AMANDA: Slow down, boy. Slow down. The bus stops here.

BONGO (*Wildly*): Miss gone! Miss gone! All gone! Plenty bad!

AMANDA: And who is Miss Gone? Any relation to mistake? Ha! Ha! (*She looks dubiously at* BONGO.) But you wouldn't get that, Bongo. I'm afraid it's a bit over your head.

BONGO: Miss gone! Miss gone! (FIG-NEWTON *and* BRIAN *enter hurriedly from right. Both are agitated.*)

AMANDA: Say, what's happening around here, anyway? I just dropped by to wish you luck on your hunt today.

FIG-NEWTON (*Gloomily*): There won't be any beastly hunt.

BONGO: Miss gone! Miss gone!

AMANDA: What in the world is he trying to say?

BRIAN: It's Hermione! She's disappeared! (*He holds his head in his hands, the picture of dejection.*)

AMANDA: Disappeared! How frightful!

BRIAN: It must have happened during the night. (*Dramatically*) Oh, I shall never forgive myself! I promised to protect her—with my life if necessary—and now she is gone. I am a disgrace to the Empire! What if the British consul at Mogala should hear of this!

FIG-NEWTON: Stiff upper lip, old boy—stiff upper lip.

BONGO: Miss gone!

FIG-NEWTON: Foul play, that's what it is! Some signs of a struggle in the tent. She sleeps in the tent with my wife.

AMANDA: But didn't Mrs. Fig-Newton hear anything?

FIG-NEWTON: Not a thing. Slept like a blasted top. Most unusual. Ordinarily a light sleeper. (*Sighs deeply*)

BRIAN: Personally, I think she was drugged. (*Quick look right and left*)

FIG-NEWTON: Must be the work of those dratted Marilyn Mau-Maus. (*Quick look right and left*)

AMANDA: They're still restless in the village, I can tell you that. There's monkey business afoot. (*Going toward right*) I'd better have a look at Mrs. Fig-Newton. (AMANDA *exits.*)

FIG-NEWTON: Question before the house is—what do we do now? Can't have this sort of thing, you know. Simply isn't cricket. A man's daughter should be safe in her own tent. (*Shouting*) The Prime Minister shall hear of this.

BRIAN (*Grabbing him by arm*): We must search for her. And the obvious place is the village itself. There will be danger, but I for one shall laugh at it. Ha! Ha! We'll go armed. I'll get my gun. (*Takes several long strides*)

FIG-NEWTON: So shall I. (*Strides about stage during speech*) Makes my blood boil, this sort of thing. An insult to the Union Jack. We Fig-Newtons aren't accustomed to such treatment.

BONGO: Miss gone!

BRIAN: Find Tongo, Bongo, and fetch him here at once.

BONGO (*Shrugging*): No sabbee.

BRIAN (*With exasperation*): Hungala sama Tongo!

BONGO (*Nodding*): Sabbee! Hungala! (*He exits right. AMANDA and* MRS. FIG-NEWTON *enter at right.* AMANDA *has her arm around the latter.* MRS. FIG-NEWTON, *looking very dazed, keeps sinking to the ground.*)

FIG-NEWTON: Oh, I say, old girl, you look in frightfully bad shape! Let me give you a hand. (*He and* AMANDA *help* MRS. FIG-NEWTON, *with difficulty, to a camp stool. She sinks onto it. Then she falls off, and they help her onto it again.*)

AMANDA: Drugged all right. Smell it? (FIG-NEWTON *sniffs and shudders*) Oh, that's the ointment you're whiffing. Horrible, isn't it? But the odor I mean is chloroform. Though how anybody in these parts got hold of chloroform is more than I know. (MRS. FIG-NEWTON, *slumping on the stool, begins to sing, off-tune,* "*I'm Dreaming of a White Christmas.*")

FIG-NEWTON: Steady, old girl—steady.

AMANDA (*Opening her bag*): I'll try to bring her out of it. Anything to stop that singing. Spirits of ammonia should help. (*Looking into bag*) Hello, what's this? My chloroform is missing!

BRIAN: That explains it!

AMANDA (*Holding open bottle to* MRS. FIG-NEWTON'S *nose*): Take a good whiff now, and you'll be clear-headed in a jiffy. (*To the others*) Some sneaking thief has been at my bag.

MRS. FIG-NEWTON: For they have crowned me Queen of the May, dear Mother!

AMANDA: Another whiff now.

MRS. FIG-NEWTON (*Shaking her head and blinking her eyes in bewilderment*): Oh! Where am I?

AMANDA: In the dear old jungle.

MRS. FIG-NEWTON: But what has happened to me?

AMANDA: You've been chloroformed, that's what.

FIG-NEWTON: Recall anything about last night, old girl? Most important that you think.

MRS. FIG-NEWTON: Last night? (*She rubs her hand over her forehead and then slumps again on stool. She begins to sing tunelessly "Home on the Range."* AMANDA *gives her another whiff of ammonia.*)

FIG-NEWTON: Now—about last night, old girl?

MRS. FIG-NEWTON: Last night? (*Suddenly awake*) Why, of course. (*Excitedly*) Someone came into the tent—and then, without any warning, someone placed a sort of cloth over my face. That is the last I remember.

FIG-NEWTON: And that's jolly well enough. Just what we suspected. (*The native drums begin to beat.*)

AMANDA: There they go again. (*Looks right and left*)

FIG-NEWTON: Blast them! But we'll fix them this time. Jolly impolite to take a man's daughter away from him.

MRS. FIG-NEWTON: Hermione! Where is she?

BRIAN: She's disappeared. But please control yourself. We shall do all in our power to get her back. That I promise you. (*Holds up right hand as if taking an oath.* BONGO *and* TONGO *enter right.*) Ah, Tongo, you know what has happened, of course?

TONGO: I am fully aware of the circumstances, sir. (*To* MRS. FIG-NEWTON) You have my profoundest sympathy, madam. (*To* FIG-NEWTON) And you, sir.

FIG-NEWTON: Dashed decent of you, Tongo, dashed decent. (*Bows head*)

TONGO: Brian, I have never forgotten what I owe you. But for you, I should have been food for a lion. I think that in this bitter hour, I can be of help. After all, I know my people. If you and Mr. Fig-Newton will come with me, I shall tell you much of interest on the way.

BRIAN: We knew we could rely on you, Tongo. (*To* BONGO) Bongo, get our guns. Kananda buzzaka. (BONGO *exits.*) I shall gladly give my life to save the one I love. (*Places his hand over his heart. The four* NATIVES *enter from right. The leader stops at center.*)

LEADER: Bwana! Boona! (*The* SMALL NATIVE *carrying the bucket seems unusually happy. He is grinning broadly and ogling the bucket.*)

SMALL NATIVE: Yum! Yum!

AMANDA: Great heavens, do you suppose that Hermione is literally in the soup? (*Looks into bucket*) The natives have a little joke. One says to the other, "What soup was that we had last night?" and the other says, "That was no soup—that was your Uncle Bimbo."

FIG-NEWTON (*Bewildered*): Don't get, it old thing. Quite beyond me.

MRS. FIG-NEWTON: But how horrible! Do you really think—

BRIAN (*Looking into bucket, wildly*): Hermione, speak to me, darling! Speak to me!

FIG-NEWTON (*Grabbing his arm and leading him away*): Stiff upper lip, old man. Stiff upper . . .

SMALL NATIVE (*Still grinning*): Yum! Yum! (*The four* NATIVES *exit left in single file.* BONGO *enters at right with two guns.* BRIAN *has covered his face with his hands.*)

TONGO: Be brave, Brian, my friend. All is not lost.

BRIAN: But if the British consul should hear of this!

FIG-NEWTON: Will you stay here with my wife, Dr. Strait-lace?

AMANDA: Glad to. And if you catch the crook who filched my chloroform, sock him on the nose for me.

FIG-NEWTON: You stay, too, Bongo, old fellow.

BONGO: No sabbee.

TONGO: Kabala naba goma.

BONGO (*Smiling*): Sabbee. Kabala.

BRIAN (*Recovering*): Hand me my gun. (BONGO *hands him gun, which* BRIAN *shoulders.*) And now on to rescue the fairest flower of England!

AMANDA (*Shouts*): Good luck to you. And don't forget that sock on the nose. (BRIAN, FIG-NEWTON, *and* TONGO *exit right.*)

MRS. FIG-NEWTON (*Wiping her eyes with handkerchief*): How ghastly this all is!

AMANDA: Cheer up, Mrs. Fig-Newton. (*Slaps her on back*) It's always darkest before the dawn. And bucket or no bucket, I have a hunch your daughter is going to be all right.

MRS. FIG-NEWTON: How I hope so! (*A strange* NATIVE *enters at left. He is dressed like* BONGO *and* TONGO, *but around his neck is a gold trinket, and on his arms are gold bracelets.* MRS.

FIG-NEWTON *looks startled, and* AMANDA *eyes the* NATIVE *with deep suspicion. The* NATIVE *speaks to* BONGO.)

NATIVE: Cumala sama gogo. Subgum soomoo haga.

BONGO: Gogo soomoo. Kamala togo.

AMANDA: Who is this creature, anyway? He looks like a walking ad for the corner jewelry store.

BONGO: Him Cromo.

NATIVE: Me speak your tongue.

AMANDA: Now isn't that nice. What do you want?

NATIVE: Me come from chief. Him much angry. Beegin-Beegeen gone. Him say white men go. If no go, be plenty kill. (*Finger across throat*)

AMANDA: Your chief sounds like a jolly soul. So he wants the Fig-Newtons to clear out, hey?

NATIVE: Wants go.

MRS. FIG-NEWTON: And what about my daughter? Your chief has kidnapped her.

NATIVE (*Shrugging shoulders*): No catch.

AMANDA: Tell him, Bongo. You know the story—Miss gone! Miss gone!

BONGO: Sabbee. Kuraga kabala kamagi. Sumapi tongto. Sumapi wongo.

NATIVE (*Angrily*): Salawala gogo togo wogo.

BONGO: Him not know miss. Never see.

AMANDA: A likely story. (*Goes to* NATIVE *and fingers one of his bracelets*) Gold!

MRS. FIG-NEWTON: Real gold?

AMANDA: Positively. (*To* NATIVE) Where did you get all this stuff, anyway? Pretty expensive items for a fellow like you to be decked out in.

NATIVE (*Smiling and fingering bracelets*): Like?

AMANDA: They're lovely.

NATIVE: You take. (*He removes bracelet and gives it to her*) Plenty more.

AMANDA: Plenty?

NATIVE: Marilyn Mau-Mau tribe have much in ground. No worth much. Goggle say so.

AMANDA: Aha! So that gargoyle, Goggle, says so. He's a smart cookie, that one!

NATIVE: Goggle take much. Give plenty for it.

AMANDA: I'll bet. Beads and combs and brushes and really valuable stuff like that in exchange for just some poor old worthless gold. He's got a big heart, Goggle has. Anyway, thanks for the bracelet, Mr. Tiffany.

NATIVE: Now you go. All go. Make chief happy.

MRS. FIG-NEWTON: And what about my daughter?

NATIVE: Not know her.

MRS. FIG-NEWTON: Blonde girl, very good looking, nice complexion—

BONGO: Miss gone!

AMANDA: We're just going around in a circle. I honestly believe this jewelry salesman doesn't know anything about Hermione. (FIG-NEWTON, BRIAN, TONGO, *and* GOGGLE *enter at right, followed by* HERMIONE. GOGGLE *has his hands tied behind his back.* BRIAN *is carrying a small wooden idol.*)

BRIAN: Here's your daughter, safe and sound.

HERMIONE: Mother! (*She rushes to embrace* MRS. FIG-NEWTON.)

MRS. FIG-NEWTON (*Overwhelmed*): My darling child! I'm so thankful you were spared. (*Weeps*) We thought you might be in—in the soup.

FIG-NEWTON (*Patting his wife and daughter*): Couldn't have that, you know. These chaps put too much pepper and okra in their soups. Englishmen never did go in for heavy seasoning.

AMANDA: Jolly good thing the natives never sampled a fig-newton. I hate to think of the epitaph we might have written: "Hermione Fig-Newton, Good to the Last Munch."

FIG-NEWTON: Gad, Elizabeth, you won't believe what's happened. Couldn't occur in England, you know. We've law and order there.

BRIAN: The law here will take care of this villain.

AMANDA: So Goggle is the snake in the grass!

NATIVE: Hello, Goggle.

GOGGLE (*Shouts*): Shut your bloomin' trap.

AMANDA: Mind your manners, Goggle. This Cromo here is a sweet fellow. Gives away gold and everything, but I suspect you know all about that.

TONGO: Ah, yes, the lurid details about Goggle have come to light. You see, he did not want any of you in this area. He was afraid you would discover my people have a great deal of gold, although they do not know the value of it. He has had a profitable time among them—trading worthless baubles for the gold.

FIG-NEWTON: Disgraceful! And an insult to the Queen! (*Salutes*)

BRIAN (*Removing helmet*): The Queen—God bless her!

TONGO: So he disseminated rumors among my people. He stole Beegin-Beegeen and cast suspicion on all of you. Then, in order to strike terror among you, he kidnapped Miss Hermione last night. We found much gold, Beegin-Beegeen, and Miss Hermione in his tent.

AMANDA: And I'll bet you swiped the chloroform from my bag, Goggle. (*She goes over to him and slaps his face. He winces.*) I thought there was something fishy about you. Yes, sir, as fishy as a can of tuna.

FIG-NEWTON: Oh, I say, that's frightfully good! Ha! Ha! As fishy as a can of tuna. I must remember that. It'll make a big splash at the club. Ha! Ha!

HERMIONE: Brian was wonderful, Mother. When Goggle tried to escape, Brian simply overpowered him.

BRIAN: My strength was as the strength of *ten*, because I was doing it for you, Hermione.

HERMIONE: Oh, Brian! (*She comes to him, and they embrace.*)

FIG-NEWTON: Splendid! A jolly sight when two English hearts are one!

NATIVE (*Excitedly*): Look. Beegin-Beegeen! (*He takes idol from* BRIAN, *bows his head to idol, and closes his eyes.*)

TONGO: Sakala mongo Beegin-Beegeen.

NATIVE (*Smiling*): Sakala! Mogaway logo bogo togo. (*He exits happily left, with idol.*)

TONGO: He will take the idol to the chief and explain all. And I do not think you will be bothered further by the drums. (*Drums have begun to beat once more in a different rhythm.*)

MRS. FIG-NEWTON: That's the second happiest bit of news I've had today. (GOGGLE *suddenly tries to make a dash for right. He gets almost to exit, but* BRIAN *grabs his shoulders, pins him to the ground, and sits on him.*)

BRIAN: Oh, no you don't, Goggle. We'll be taking you to the magistrates at Mogala.

GOGGLE: I'd like to get my 'ands on you. You've spoiled the chance of a lifetime.

BRIAN: Sit on him, Bongo.

BONGO (*Coming over*): Me sit.

MRS. FIG-NEWTON: I think we all ought to have a nice cup of tea.

FIG-NEWTON: Dashed good idea, old girl. And tomorrow, it's off to bag a lion. (*The drums suddenly cease.*)

TONGO: Ah, Cromo has accomplished his mission.

GOGGLE: And I 'ope you all get eaten by lions in the mornin'.

FIG-NEWTON: That's not courteous, old man, not courteous at all.

GOGGLE: I wasn't aimin' to be polite.

FIG-NEWTON: Well, you should, old boy—you should. Civility keeps the British Empire alive, you know.

GOGGLE: Nuts to the Empire.

HERMIONE: Want to help me prepare the tea, Brian?

BRIAN: It will be heaven, Hermione. (*They exit hand in hand.*)

AMANDA: Now there's a handsome couple.

FIG-NEWTON: English, you know. Shows in the bearing, don't you think?

AMANDA (*Good-humoredly*): No question about it.

FIG-NEWTON: Tongo and Bongo, I suggest you two fellows tie up this blighter, Goggle, in my tent where I'll be able to keep an eye on him.

TONGO: A first-rate idea, sir. (*He and* BONGO *get* GOGGLE *to his feet and lead him toward right.*)

GOGGLE: I 'ope you all choke on your blasted tea! (*He,* BONGO, *and* TONGO *exit.*)

FIG-NEWTON: No one *ever* choked on good English tea. Absolute impossibility, you know. (HERMIONE *and* BRIAN *enter with teapot and cups.*)

HERMIONE: There was water already boiling on the camp stove, so here we are.

BRIAN: Let's all sit down. (*They sit at table.*)

HERMIONE: Oh, I'm so happy.

AMANDA: And so you should be. Brian's a handsome young fellow.

BRIAN: But not worthy of Hermione.

HERMIONE: Why, Brian Broadbow, of course you are.

FIG-NEWTON (*In the act of sipping his tea, suddenly begins to choke with laughter*): Oh! That is good!

HERMIONE (*Startled*): What is it, Father?

FIG-NEWTON (*Unable to control his laughter*): That was no soup—that was your Uncle Bimbo! Oh, jolly good. I must remember that at the club.

AMANDA: Well, better late than never. And if you want to give the lions a good laugh tomorrow, you might tell them, too. (FIG-NEWTON *continues to laugh, and the four* NATIVES, *led by the tall one in the white chef's hat, enter. The leader carries a sign reading:* RECOMMENDED BY HUNCAN DINES. *They file solemnly across the stage as the curtain falls.*)

THE END

Production Notes

THE NATIVES ARE RESTLESS TONIGHT

Characters: 10 male; 3 female.

Playing Time: 30 minutes.

Costumes: Fig-Newton and Brian Broadbow wear shorts, thick knee-length socks, shirts and sun helmets. When Fig-Newton re-appears in Scene 1, he has changed to formal evening attire. Hermione wears a white skirt and blouse, heavy walking shoes and a sun helmet. Goggle wears shorts, a rather dirty shirt and a black derby. Amanda is dressed in white. Mrs. Fig-Newton wears an evening gown in Scene 1; in Scene 2, she may wear a fancy negligee. The natives wear ridiculous yellow wigs and colorful shorts. They are barefooted and their bodies may be painted with colorful designs. Cromo is covered with gold jewelry. The leader of the four natives wears a white chef's hat.

Properties: Scene 1: Handkerchief for Fig-Newton; bucket with steam coming out for little native; black doctor's bag for Amanda (the bag should contain various instruments, bottles and tubes); bowls of soup. Scene 2: bottle; two guns; small wooden idol; teapot and cups; sign, RECOMMENDED BY HUNCAN DINES, for tall native.

Setting: A camp in a jungle clearing. Exotic foliage may be placed in the background to suggest the dense jungle atmosphere. At center is a crude wooden table, set with four places. There are canvas-bottomed chairs at the table. Down left and right are wooden benches.

Lighting: No special effects.

Sound: Native drums. Occasional offstage calls of jungle birds and animals may also be used.

Abner Crane from Hayseed Lane

Characters

ELIZA RHODE, *a plump, pleasant, middle-aged woman*
GLORY RHODE, *her beautiful daughter*
GRISELDA, *the awkward hired girl*
DANIEL J. LOOPHOLE, *the suave villain*
QUIGLEY W. QUACK, *his cynical accomplice*
ABNER CRANE, *the country bumpkin*
GWENDOLYN, *a waitress*
FIFI LATOUR, *a striking-looking, slinky young woman*
CONSTABLE PERKINS

SCENE 1

TIME: *Late morning of a June day in the 1890's.*
SETTING: *The living room of the Rhode farm in Snaggletooth, Vermont.*
AT RISE: ELIZA RHODE *is seated at left of the table. She is stirring a large basin on her lap with a wooden spoon.* GLORY *is seated on the sofa mending a pair of stockings.*

GLORY: Mercy, Mother, these stockings of yours are as full of holes as that new-fangled Swiss cheese which that nice

Mr. Loophole brought us the other day. You'll be needing a new pair, I'm thinking.

ELIZA (*Gloomily*): Stockings cost money, Glory, and there's not much of that in Snaggletooth, Vermont, right now.

GLORY: I don't recollect ever having so lean a year on the farm.

ELIZA: No, things haven't been the same since your Paw passed on five years ago. Life isn't easy for a poor widow.

GLORY: Have you thought of accepting Mr. Loophole's offer, Mother?

ELIZA: Which offer?

GLORY: Doesn't he want to buy the farm for five thousand dollars?

ELIZA: Oh, that offer.

GLORY: You mean there's been another?

ELIZA (*Archly*): Sure has. He's made an offer for your hand.

GLORY: He wants to marry me?

ELIZA: It certainly isn't me he wants.

GLORY: Why, Mother, you never told me.

ELIZA: You never asked. And I'm not one to do a lot of gabbin'. How do you feel toward him, Glory?

GLORY (*Hesitantly*): Well—he's a gentleman, that's for sure. And he does have a way with him.

ELIZA: But I'll bet your heart is still set on Abner Crane from Hayseed Lane. Is that it, child?

GLORY: Well—

ELIZA: Abner's goin' to drop by today. I want his advice about this farm business. He's quiet, but he's deep.

GLORY: Yes, Abner's sweet.

ELIZA: Trouble with Abner is he's so shy. Come to think of it, he's about the most bashful man around women I ever did see.

GLORY: Well, Mr. Loophole isn't—bashful, I mean.

ELIZA: Gracious, no. Why, that Mr. Loophole could charm a hen right off her eggs with his fancy talk. And, speakin' of hens, I guess this feed is about ready for 'em now. Where's Griselda?

GLORY: I think she's in the kitchen.

ELIZA: She's never around when you want her. Fact is, she's so clumsy she's not much use as a hired girl. But she's an orphan, and somebody has to look after her.

GLORY: And she means well, poor thing.

ELIZA: Griselda! (GRISELDA, *the hired girl, rushes in from right. She comes in so fast that she stumbles and falls flat on her face. GRISELDA'S chief trouble is that she seems to have two left feet. She is awkward but good-natured. She is bare-footed, wears a dress and apron, has wild-looking, unkempt hair, and speaks loudly.*)

GRISELDA: Oops! I slipped!

ELIZA: Pick yourself up, child, and take this feed for the hens. (GRISELDA *rises, comes to* ELIZA, *takes feed, drops it on floor, scrambles down to her hands and knees and begins to pick it up.*)

GRISELDA: I'm sorry!

ELIZA: Well, if the hens don't object, I won't. (GRISELDA *takes basin of feed, goes to center door, opens it, and throws out contents. A loud voice outside yells, "Ouch!" Another voice laughs raucously.*)

ELIZA: Mercy! What's that? (DANIEL J. LOOPHOLE, *a tall, suave man sporting a handsome mustache, enters. His clothes are covered with chicken feed, and he is wiping his eyes with his handkerchief. He is followed by his companion, QUIGLEY W. QUACK, a short, stout, cynical-looking fellow who is obviously enjoying* LOOPHOLE'S *discomfort.*)

QUACK: Got you right in the eye, Daniel. Even William Tell couldn't have aimed more accurately.

LOOPHOLE: Control yourself, Quigley.

QUACK: Quigley W. Quack is always in control of himself.

GRISELDA: Why, Mr. Loophole, I'm real sorry. Guess I mistook you for one of the roosters.

QUACK (*Laughing*): A rooster! Wonderful! She's got you there, Daniel.

LOOPHOLE (*Stooping to kiss* ELIZA's *hand*): My dear Mrs. Eliza Rhode, a bit of discomfort in the home of so captivating a woman is easily forgiven. (*To* GLORY) Ah, Miss Rhode, as usual, you are blooming like the fairest of roses.

GLORY: Thank you, Mr. Loophole.

LOOPHOLE: My friend Quack and I have been walking by the river. Ah, what a perfectly beautiful morning! Everything is budding as though a new mantle of hope had been spread over the earth.

ELIZA (*Matter-of-factly*): Yep, the Snaggletooth River is mighty purty this time of year. Do sit down, Mr. Loophole and Mr. Quack. You must be tired from your walk.

LOOPHOLE (*Goes to chair at right of table, while* QUACK *goes to sofa*): Thank you, madam. Thank you, indeed. Although, to speak truly, I am never fatigued by mild exercise and nature's bountiful wonders. As the poet has said, "And what is so rare as a day in June?"

ELIZA: You sure got a head for that poetry stuff, Mr. Loophole. (*Just as* LOOPHOLE *is about to sit*, GRISELDA *moves the chair backward.*)

GRISELDA (*Using her apron as a dustcloth*): I'll just give the seat a dusting before you sit. (LOOPHOLE, *not noticing, goes to sit down and lands on his posterior on the floor.*)

QUACK: This just isn't your day, Daniel.

ELIZA: Oh, mercy me, Griselda. Now see what you've done!

GRISELDA: I was just trying to help. After all, I'm only a poor orphan girl. (*She bursts into tears and runs off right.*)

GLORY: Poor child. She means so well.

LOOPHOLE (*Getting up and sitting down*): No harm done. (*To* ELIZA) Have you given my offer due consideration, my dear?

ELIZA: You mean the five thousand dollars?

LOOPHOLE: That, of course—but, you will recall, there was another offer far more close to my heart. I refer to my great desire that the beautiful Miss Glory Rhode honor me with her hand in marriage so that I may devote my life to fulfilling her every whim and desire.

GLORY (*Blushing*): It's mighty nice of you, Mr. Loophole.

LOOPHOLE: Please call me Daniel.

GLORY: It's real nice of you—Daniel.

LOOPHOLE: Ah, the name on your lips is like the sweet sound of chapel bells at twilight.

ELIZA: Oh, shucks, Mr. Loophole, how you do go on. But as for marriage, that's up to Glory. All I can say is I won't stand in the way of the match. About sellin' the farm, that's a different matter. I'm not makin' up my mind till I've had a real good chat with Abner Crane from Hayseed Lane. I set a good deal of store by his common sense. Besides, I think Abner may be interested in Glory, too.

GLORY: Now, Mother, let's not exaggerate. He's never said anything about that.

ELIZA: No, I suppose he hasn't. But he's near tongue-tied when he's around females. Strange, too, because when it is not a question of romance, he's as lively as a cricket.

QUACK: Lively is right.

GLORY: Do you know Abner, Mr. Quack?

QUACK: We've made his acquaintance at the Snaggletooth Inn. He drops in every afternoon for a cup of coffee.

LOOPHOLE: Ah, yes, and he has often praised your qualities as an admirable woman.

ELIZA: That's real nice of him. Anyway, he's comin' by this mornin'. Ought to be here any time now.

QUACK: I can hardly wait.

LOOPHOLE: Mind your manners, Quigley. (*To* ELIZA) Yes, we know Mr. Crane. He has even advised us where the fishing is best, for, as you know, Mr. Quack and I are here only for the trout fishing.

QUACK: And haven't got a bite, yet.

LOOPHOLE: That is not important, Quigley. What matters is that our fishing excursion has enabled us to meet this delightful Rhode family and has made me desire to settle in Snaggletooth for the rest of my natural days. (*There is a knock at door.*)

ELIZA: Come in. (ABNER CRANE *enters. He is chewing on a blade of grass.*) Oh, it's you, Abner. We've been expectin' you.

ABNER: Yep. It's Abner Crane. (*Note:* ABNER *delivers most of his lines dead-pan.*) Say, Loophole, looks like your buggy ran over one of Mrs. Rhode's pigs down the road.

LOOPHOLE (*To* ELIZA): Do not worry, my dear Mrs. Rhode. I will replace your pig.

ABNER (*Shakes his head as he eyes* LOOPHOLE): You can't. You're not fat enough.

QUACK: You ought to be on the stage with that talent.

ELIZA: I'm glad you've come, Abner. There's a heap of things I want to talk over with you.

ABNER: Glad to help.

GLORY: You're sweet, Abner. (ABNER *hangs his head in embarrassment.*)

QUACK: Like a ten-pound box of chocolates.

ELIZA: You see, Abner, Mr. Loophole wants to buy my farm.

ABNER: Buy the farm, hey? (*Sharply*) How much does he offer?

LOOPHOLE: Five thousand dollars—in cash—and a most fair price it is.

ABNER: That's as may be. 'Pears to me, though, when a farm's been in the family as long as this one has, it's not right to sell. Another thing's botherin' me, too. Why does a city feller like you want a farm? Just not natural. It's like a hog wantin' to settle down on Fifth Avenoo in New York City.

LOOPHOLE: Sir, are you implying that I am a hog?

ABNER: Shucks, no—you don't have the snout for it, for one thing. Feller can tell by lookin' at you, you're no hog.

LOOPHOLE: Since no insult was intended, I accept your apology.

ABNER: Wasn't apologizin'—just statin' facts.

QUACK: Facts? Well, here are some facts about farming, Crane. Anyone can farm. All it takes is a strong back and a weak mind.

ABNER: How are you fixed for a strong back, Loophole?

LOOPHOLE (*Waving him aside*): In any event, I have fallen in love with the countryside and have decided to spend my life in these fair surroundings. And I might add, it is not only the countryside that has won my heart. (*Looks pointedly at* GLORY)

ABNER (*Quickly*): You mean you been makin' eyes at Glory?

LOOPHOLE (*Dramatically*): To live in these beautiful surroundings with the most beautiful woman in the world—"'tis a consummation devoutly to be wish'd!" Ah, Glory, as I came up here this morning, I saw some cows rubbing noses in the accepted bovine fashion. And now that I behold you, I must confess I want to do the same.

ABNER: Go ahead. The cow won't mind too much.

ELIZA: Mr. Loophole has asked for Glory's hand in marriage.

ABNER: Marriage!

GLORY: I haven't made up my mind, Abner.

ABNER (*Gloomily*): Well, it's not my place to be givin' out advice about weddin's. Appears to me, though, Eliza, if you want to sell the farm, five thousand isn't much.

ELIZA: If you say so, Abner, I guess it must be so.

ABNER: Yep, a feller's got to get up pretty early in the mornin' to fool Abner Crane.

QUACK: I'll bet.

LOOPHOLE: But, of course, it is marriage and the hope of it that I nurse close to my heart.

QUACK (*Cynically*): And a manly heart it is.

LOOPHOLE: Thank you, Quigley. To settle down here with a young woman of taste—

ABNER: I got pigs that can taste.

LOOPHOLE: A young woman of beauty—

ABNER: And I got a heifer that's beautiful . . .

LOOPHOLE: A young woman with such soulful eyes—

ABNER: And you ought to see the eyes on my old gray mare.

LOOPHOLE: Bah!

ABNER: And I got a lamb that says "Bah" even clearer than you do.

GLORY: Abner, behave!

ABNER: I'm tryin'.

GLORY: I'll have to think more about marriage, Mr. Loophole.

ABNER: If everybody did more thinkin' about wedded bliss, there wouldn't be so many divorces.

QUACK: You're a rural philosopher, Mr. Crane.

ABNER: I'm a what?

QUACK: A rural philosopher.

ABNER: That doesn't sound good, but I don't aim to be insulted.

GLORY: A philosopher is a deep thinker, Abner.

ABNER: Oh, that's different. Yep, then I'm a phil—a phol— a phil-o-what-do-you-call-it.

LOOPHOLE (*Rising*): At any rate, my dear Glory, you know how I feel. We could be as happy as larks together. It would help if I could have your answer in the morning. And, my dear Mrs. Rhode, please give the sale of the farm some more thought, too. In the morning, I shall appear here with five thousand dollars in cash and a marriage license. Need I say that my fondest hope is that the latter will be the more important of the two.

ELIZA: That's real nice of you, Mr. Loophole. (GRISELDA *enters suddenly from right carrying a broom.*)

GRISELDA: I'd better sweep up them bits of chicken feed. (*She comes to center, awkwardly swings broom, and hits* LOOPHOLE *on the head with it.*)

LOOPHOLE: Ouch! Drat it, girl! Can't you look what you're doing!

GRISELDA: I'm sorry. I'm just a poor orphan girl—

QUACK: Temper, Daniel. Temper.

LOOPHOLE (*Rubbing his head*): Forgive my outburst. No harm done. (*He kisses* GLORY'S *hand and* ELIZA'S, *and then goes to center, followed by* QUACK.) Mr. Quack and I shall go back to the inn along the river. And amid the loveliness of the scenery, I shall think of your loveliness, Glory.

GLORY: Oh, Daniel.

LOOPHOLE: Goodbye, Mr. Crane.

ABNER: Don't get tuckered out with all that thinkin'. (LOOPHOLE *and* QUACK *exit*.)

ELIZA: Oh, hasn't he got the golden tongue, though!

ABNER: Gold is where you find it.

ELIZA: Then you don't think I should sell, Abner?

ABNER: Sure don't.

ELIZA: But the farm is so run-down, and times so bad.

ABNER: Times might get better.

ELIZA (*Archly*): And do you think Glory should marry Mr. Loophole?

ABNER: Don't have anything to say about that. Feller's a fool to stick his nose in other people's affairs.

ELIZA: Come, Griselda, I need your help in the kitchen. (GRISELDA *knocks over a chair with the broom*.)

GRISELDA: Oops!

ELIZA: And put that broom away before you kill somebody with it!

GRISELDA: I'll just sweep outside a moment. Then I'll help in the kitchen. (*She exits up center*. ELIZA *exits right*.)

GLORY: Abner, what about the question Mother asked you?

ABNER: Which one?

GLORY: Do you want me to marry Mr. Loophole?

ABNER (*Bashfully*): Well—can't say that I do.

GLORY: Why not, Abner?

ABNER (*Shifting uncomfortably from one foot to the other and chewing furiously on his blade of grass*): Well—well—shucks, I—

GLORY (*Determinedly*): Have you ever thought of settling down, Abner?

ABNER: Settlin'?

GLORY: With a wife. So you can have a companion.

ABNER: Shucks, I've got my pigs and cows and chickens. They keep a feller from gettin' lonesome.

GLORY: They're hardly the same as a wife.

ABNER: Well, they don't talk back at you—that's somethin'.

GLORY (*Exasperated*): Oh, Abner, you're about as romantic as a picket fence. (GRISELDA *rushes in.*)

GRISELDA: Gracious! I just hit one of the hens. I don't know whether the hen is dead or just unconscious.

ABNER: Well, Griselda, a dead hen is good for somethin'.

GRISELDA: What's that?

ABNER: To eat. (*Pulling a large watch from his overalls*) Got to be goin'. Nearly feedin' time for the hogs. (ELIZA *enters from right.*)

ELIZA: You on your way, Abner?

ABNER: Yep. (*Goes toward upstage center*)

ELIZA: Thanks for the advice. I'll think twice about sellin'.

ABNER: Guess you both have a lot of thinkin' to do. Be seein' you. (*He exits.*)

GLORY: Was there ever anyone like him? So shy when it comes to romance. Oh, why doesn't he speak?

ELIZA: Lost your heart to him, girl?

GLORY (*Exasperated*): Oh, what's the use!

ELIZA: Guess he's just not the marryin' kind. But that Mr. Loophole is. You could do worse. Anyway, 'most time for lunch. Got some nice fresh eggs.

GRISELDA (*Coughs*): Er—ma'am—there aren't any eggs.

ELIZA: What!

GRISELDA: I broke two dozen this morning.

ELIZA: Oh, Griselda!

GRISELDA: I'm just a poor orphan girl, and I— (*She continues to go on and bursts into tears.*)

CURTAIN

*   *   *   *

SCENE 2

TIME: *Five minutes later.*

SETTING: *A country road. (This scene may be played before the curtain.)*

AT RISE: LOOPHOLE *and* QUACK *enter at left on their way to the village inn.* LOOPHOLE *is cheerful,* QUACK *gloomy. They come to center.*

LOOPHOLE (*Breathing deeply*): Ah, this country air! As Wordsworth says, "One impulse from a vernal wood can teach us more of moral good than all the sages can."

QUACK: My feet hurt.

LOOPHOLE: Don't be fretful, Quigley. This is a glorious place.

QUACK: It's a hick town, and you know it.

LOOPHOLE (*Catching sight of audience*): Aha! We have company, Quigley. (*Bowing to audience*) How do you do? Lovely day, isn't it?

QUACK: My feet still hurt.

LOOPHOLE: As I look into your open, honest, intelligent faces, I know that you have been admiring my conduct at the Widow Rhode's. (*Twirling his mustache*) Clever, wasn't it? Little does she know that her farm is worth a fortune. Heh! Heh! Heh!

QUACK: You going to talk all day? I want to get back to the inn and lie on that torture rack they call a bed.

LOOPHOLE: Patience, Quigley, patience. Can't you see that I fascinate these good people? (*Grinning*) You see, my dear friends, the Tin Brothers Canning Company is going to open a branch in Snaggletooth—because of the water power. They want to purchase farms near the river, both for a factory site and for their produce. As I said to

Quigley, "Quigley, our fortune is made." Heh! Heh!

QUACK: Oh, my aching feet!

LOOPHOLE: Naturally, as an honest man—Heh! Heh! Heh!
—my first step is to get hold of land near the Snaggletooth River—land the factory will need to buy. And I'm
going to do just that. (*Snickering*) For a mere five thousand
dollars. Actually, the Rhode farm is now worth over ten
times that much. (*Confidentially*) But, of course— (*Twirling his mustache*) if the beautiful Glory marries me, the
farm won't cost me a cent. I'll just move right in. Clever,
isn't it?

QUACK: You're not backward about being forward. But
don't forget, that rube, Abner Crane, has his eyes on
Glory, too. And he's advised them against selling the
farm.

LOOPHOLE (*Laughing*): My friend is a cynic. As if a mere
country bumpkin were any match for me—Daniel J.
Loophole. In all modesty, I must admit that I have one
of the great brains of the century. Listen carefully now,
friends. I am about to make Abner Crane the laughing
stock of Snaggletooth. His reputation will not be worth
a wooden nickel. Heh! Heh! Ah, you ask, how shall I
accomplish this?

QUACK: A good question.

LOOPHOLE: It is child's play, for Abner has the brain of a
six-year-old. Arriving at the inn soon—in fact, she is
perhaps already there—is an old friend of mine, Miss
Fifi LaTour.

QUACK: And what a girl!

LOOPHOLE: How right you are, Quigley. Yes, Fifi is a
woman whom no man—except me—can resist. She and
I have concocted a plan for Abner. When it is accomplished, Miss Glory Rhode will avoid Abner as she would

a boa constrictor and Eliza Rhode will think him a fool. Heh! Heh! Now, friends, what do you think? Do I not have a razor-sharp mind?

QUIGLEY: And I have sore feet.

LOOPHOLE: Very well, Quigley. Let us on to the inn—and to Abner Crane's undoing. Thank you, dear friends, for your kind attention. (*Twirling mustache*) Soon the fair Glory and the farm will be mine.

QUACK: And don't forget, I want my ten per cent.

LOOPHOLE: Isn't he a caution? So mercenary. Quigley, remember: money has ruined many a man.

QUACK: If I'm going to be ruined, I'd rather have money do it than anything I can think of.

LOOPHOLE: Well, friends, I bid you a fond farewell. Daniel J. Loophole is going onward to another great triumph. (*Twirls mustache*) Come, Quigley. Heh! Heh! Heh! (*They exit right*, QUACK *limping visibly*.)

CURTAIN

* * * *

SCENE 3

TIME: *Early in the afternoon of the same day.*

SETTING: *The public room of the Snaggletooth Inn.* (*This scene can also be played before the curtain, since all that is needed are a table and two chairs.*)

AT RISE: ABNER *is seated at the table. He snaps his fingers.*

ABNER: Gwendolyn! Where are you? Haven't got all day, you know. A little service would be real comfortin'. (GWENDOLYN, *the waitress, enters from right.*)

GWENDOLYN: I hear you, Abner Crane. A body can't get a bit of rest around here. Coffee as usual?

ABNER: Yep. Coffee's what I want, Gwendolyn.

GWENDOLYN: And coffee it'll be. (*She exits. In a moment or two,* FIFI LATOUR *enters from left. She is a striking-looking young woman, heavily made up, rather slinky in manner, and wearing large earrings.*)

ABNER (*Rising politely*): Howdy.

FIFI (*Passing her hand over her forehead*): Oh, sir, I am so tired.

ABNER: You look plumb tuckered out. Better sit down. (*He helps her to opposite chair at table where she sits with a sigh.*) Reckon the weight of them earrings is enough to tire even a mule. (FIFI *places her small purse on table.*)

FIFI: Oh, sir, it is not the earrings. Alas, no. It is that I am alone, penniless, and frightened.

ABNER (*Kindly*): Shucks, there is nothin' in Snaggletooth to be afraid of. (GWENDOLYN *enters with* ABNER'S *coffee. She looks suspiciously at* FIFI.)

GWENDOLYN: Who's your friend, Abner?

ABNER: Don't know her name.

FIFI: My name, kind sir, is Fifi LaTour.

ABNER: Say, sounds like somethin' right from gay Paree. Better get her a mite of coffee, too, Gwendolyn.

GWENDOLYN: If you say so, Abner. (*She exits.*)

ABNER: Somehow, don't seem that a girl like you belongs here in Snaggletooth.

FIFI: Mine is a sad story, sir. You see, I was on my way to Canada where my poor mother lies ill and penniless in the city of Montreal. But, alas, I did not have enough money for my railroad fare, and the conductor made me get off the train here in Snaggletooth.

ABNER: Say, that's a shame.

FIFI (*Reaching across table and grasping* ABNER'S *hand*): Oh, sir, you are so kind, so understanding—

ABNER (*Bashfully pulling away his hand*): Shucks!

FIFI: I knew the moment I saw you that you were one of nature's noblemen. (GWENDOLYN *enters with* FIFI'S *coffee and places it on table. She looks suspiciously at* FIFI *again and then exits.*)

FIFI (*Sipping coffee*): Ah, I needed that. How good you are to buy it for me!

ABNER: It's nothing. I can afford it. I'm not aimin' to brag, but I just sold a parcel of land for eight hundred dollars. (*He touches right hand pocket of his overalls.*)

FIFI: I knew at once that you were a brainy man.

ABNER (*Bashfully*): Shucks.

FIFI (*Rubbing her right eye*): Oh!

ABNER: What's the matter, Miss?

FIFI: I seem to have something in my eye. It must be a cinder from that horrible train ride. (*She picks up her purse, rises and comes slinkily to* ABNER.) Would you remove it for me?

ABNER: The eye?

FIFI: The cinder, please.

ABNER: Well, I'm no doctor, but I'll try. (*He rises, and takes a gaudy red bandanna from his pocket.* FIFI *snuggles closer to him.* ABNER *hangs his head in embarrassment.*)

FIFI: You're not afraid of me, are you, kind sir?

ABNER: Well, shucks, that's mighty powerful perfume you're usin'.

FIFI: You like it?

ABNER: Well, I'll say one thing for it—it's noticeable.

FIFI (*Again rubbing eye*): Oh!

ABNER: Guess I'd better get at it. (*She opens the eye wide and*

gets very close to him. He is obviously uncomfortable. While
ABNER *is looking into her eye,* FIFI *stealthily puts her hand in*
his overalls pocket and draws out what looks like a roll of money
around which is an elastic band. She transfers this to a pocket of
her dress. Then she places her small purse in ABNER'S *overalls*
pocket.)

ABNER: I can't see no dirt in there.

FIFI: Thank you, sir. It seems to be all right now. (*She*
moves closer to him.) Thank you. (*He backs up and falls into*
his chair.)

ABNER: Better drink up that coffee before it gets cold.
(FIFI *returns to other chair.*)

FIFI: My purse! My purse!

ABNER: What's the matter?

FIFI: My purse is gone! Oh, sir, and I trusted you so. How
could you take advantage of a poor, defenseless girl!

ABNER: Say, what is this?

FIFI: Help! Help!

ABNER: You got no call to be screamin' like a wet hen.
(GWENDOLYN *rushes in.*)

GWENDOLYN: What in tarnation's goin' on here?

FIFI: He stole my purse!

GWENDOLYN: Abner Crane never stole a dime in his life.

FIFI: Help! Help!

GWENDOLYN: Constable Perkins is right outside, Abner. I'll
get him. He'll straighten things out. Glory Rhode's here,
too. Her and me are goin' to Ludlow for a strawberry
supper. (*She exits right.*)

FIFI: And to think that I confided in you. (*She rises and comes*
to him.) Take that! (*She slaps his face. Then when footsteps*
are heard nearby, she throws her arms around him, kisses him,
and pretends to struggle as GLORY, GWENDOLYN, *and* CON-
STABLE PERKINS *enter, followed by* LOOPHOLE *and* QUACK.)

GLORY (*Astounded by the sight of* ABNER *seemingly trying to embrace* FIFI): Why, Abner Crane! How could you! (CONSTABLE PERKINS, *who is tall, thin, and has chin whiskers and old-fashioned spectacles, comes to* ABNER.)

CONSTABLE: Abner, what kind of goin's on are these?

FIFI: He tried to kiss me. First he stole my purse and then he forced his attentions on me.

GLORY: Oh, Abner. I hope I never see you again.

LOOPHOLE (*Putting his arm around her*): Come, my dear. Let me take you away from this scene. It is not fit for delicate feminine eyes. (*He takes her out, followed by* QUACK.)

ABNER: Glory—wait a minute, I—

FIFI: You beast! (*She slaps him again.*)

CONSTABLE: Well, Abner—seems like you got a heap of explainin' to do. (ABNER *begins to speak loudly as he exits.*)

* * * *

SCENE 4

TIME: *The next day.*

SETTING: *Same as Scene 1.*

AT RISE: GRISELDA *is dusting and knocks a vase of flowers onto the floor.*

GRISELDA: Oops!

ELIZA (*Entering from left*): Now what in the name of heaven have you done, Griselda?

GRISELDA: I was just dusting.

ELIZA: Well, wipe up the mess. I want things tidy when Mr. Loophole and Mr. Quack get here.

GRISELDA (*Kneeling on floor*): I'll fix everything.

ELIZA: And please be careful.

GLORY (*Entering from right and looking dejected*): Well, this is the day.

ELIZA: Still frettin' about what you seen yesterday, Glory? I just can't believe it of Abner to be taken with a brazen hussy. Isn't like him at all.

GLORY: It was terrible, Mother. He had his arms around her, and she was struggling—

ELIZA: And I always thought he was the bashful type.

GLORY: Are you going to sell the farm?

ELIZA: Can't make up my mind. Could do a lot with five thousand dollars, I suppose. Herman Sprout wants to sell his general store. Thought I might buy it. There's good livin' quarters over it. Be a mighty cosy place to spend my last years. (*There is a knock at center door.*) That must be Mr. Loophole and Mr. Quack. You decided about his proposal, Glory?

GLORY: Oh, I just can't make up my mind.

ELIZA: He's a fine figure of a man. (GRISELDA *rises from floor and goes to open door.* LOOPHOLE *and* QUACK *enter.*)

LOOPHOLE: Good morning. Good morning. How bright and shining you all look.

ELIZA: Come in and sit down. (LOOPHOLE *is carrying a black bag. He and* QUACK *go to sofa and sit.*)

LOOPHOLE: And this is the hour of decision. (*Patting bag*) I have in this bag five thousand dollars in cash. (*He reaches into pocket and removes a large paper.*) And here—oh sweet and sentimental document—a marriage license. (*He waves it.*) Of course, if you decide to marry me, Miss Rhode, I shall live here, run your farm, and be delighted to welcome your fair mother under our roof. (GRISELDA *exits left with fragments of the vase and flowers.*)

QUACK: A comfortable arrangement.

LOOPHOLE: Right you are, Quigley. And now, Miss Rhode

—or Glory, if I may be so bold—am I to be honored far above my just deserts by your lovely hand in marriage?

GLORY: I—well—well—I just don't know.

LOOPHOLE: But, my dear, surely you have thought about this, surely— (ABNER *suddenly enters at up center.*)

ABNER: It's friend Abner, Eliza. And my advice is to sell the farm.

GLORY: Why, Abner Crane. Do you have the audacity to appear here after what I saw yesterday. Kissing that woman—

ABNER: Now, wait a minute, Glory. There's no reason to fly off the handle before you know the facts.

GLORY (*Acidly*): I *saw* the facts.

ABNER: You haven't seen all of them, I can tell you that. So can Loophole here.

LOOPHOLE (*Coughing*): Er—I don't know what you mean, Mr. Crane.

ABNER: You know all right—sure as tarnation. But important things first. Eliza, you'd better sell the farm.

GLORY: Don't listen to him, Mother. His word means nothing any more.

ELIZA: Well, Abner—you have me all mixed up. Yesterday you said don't sell—now you say sell.

LOOPHOLE: Constancy is obviously not one of Mr. Crane's virtues—in women or in business.

GLORY: I'm not sure he has *any* virtues. Abner, I think you'd better go now.

ABNER: Sell the farm and sell it quick, Eliza. (*Sharply*) Of course, maybe—Loophole here is just fakin'. Maybe he doesn't intend to buy the farm, anyway. Maybe he figures on gettin' it the easy way by marryin' Glory.

LOOPHOLE: Sir, I object to these base insinuations.

QUACK: You tell him, Daniel.

ABNER: I'm not insinuatin'. I'm statin'.

LOOPHOLE: Mr. Crane, I would have you know that all my life I have been guided by one great principle: nothing that is false will ever do me good.

ABNER: You forgettin' about your teeth?

LOOPHOLE (*Exasperated and goaded into acting*): Very well, Mr. Crane. I shall prove to you that Daniel J. Loophole is a man of honor. (*He rises and goes to center table. He takes a paper from his pocket.*) Here is the bill of sale and deed drawn up by your own lawyer, Mrs. Rhode. Once both of us sign this document, and the money changes hands, the transaction will be legal and irrevocable.

ABNER: Ir-irrevocable?

LOOPHOLE: That simply means that everything will be final and unchangeable.

ABNER: Say, that's quite a word to mean all that. You'd better be careful about talkin' so much around here come summer, Loophole. It gets pretty hot in these parts. You're liable to get a sunburned tongue. (*Turns to* ELIZA) Well, better sign the paper right now, Eliza.

GRISELDA: I'll get the pen and ink. (*She rushes out and returns almost at once with quill-pen and ink, placing them on table.* LOOPHOLE *gives* ELIZA *the document, which she signs. Then he signs, too.*)

LOOPHOLE (*Opening bag with a flourish and beginning to remove piles of money*): And here is the five thousand dollars. (*Hands* ELIZA *the money*) The farm is now mine, and what do you think of that, Mr. Abner Crane?

ELIZA: Oh, doesn't it look lovely!

ABNER: So now everything's legal, isn't it?

LOOPHOLE: Solid and unchangeable as the Rock of Gibraltar.

QUACK: And that's pretty solid.

ABNER: Then I think there's somethin' you ought to know, Mr. Loophole. There's no cannin' company ever goin' to pay you a red cent for this farm.

LOOPHOLE: What's that? (*Somewhat flustered*) Who said anything about a canning company?

ABNER: You're not pullin' the wool over my eyes, Loophole. I wasn't born yesterday. I sold a parcel of land myself to the Tin Brothers' Cannin' Company. There's one thing about this farm you never did discover, though.

LOOPHOLE: I doubt it, my good man.

QUACK (*Uncomfortably*): I'm beginning to wonder.

ABNER: Just about a third of this farm—fact is, all the land near the river—is underwater for a good three months of the year. Guess there's no cannin' factory wants its workers drowned every spring.

LOOPHOLE: So that's it. Well, let me tell you something, my bright Mr. Crane. I happen to have checked all that. And the marker which shows how high the river rises is placed only about ten yards from the river.

ABNER: That's right.

LOOPHOLE: So you're wrong.

ABNER: No, I'm not. I put the marker there myself when I heard you was inquirin' about the farm. Thought it might help Eliza get a good price.

LOOPHOLE (*Angrily*): You put it there?

ABNER: Sure did. Moved it at least five hundred yards.

LOOPHOLE: You swindler! (CONSTABLE PERKINS *enters suddenly upstage center.*)

CONSTABLE: It's swindlers I'm after.

ELIZA: Why, Constable, what brings you here?

CONSTABLE: Got to take this here Loophole and Quack into

custody. Their friend, Fifi LaTour, has done a good bit of talkin' about them and the way they make a dishonest livin'. They were all in cahoots.

QUACK: I told you. Never trust a woman.

LOOPHOLE: There's some mistake.

CONSTABLE: There sure is, and you made it. Better come quietly. I got a couple of my men outside—and they're mighty strong fellows.

LOOPHOLE: This transaction must be voided.

ABNER: Nope, the money belongs to Eliza. You said your-self the whole thing is ir-ir—

GLORY: Irrevocable.

ABNER: That's it. That's what I mean. (CONSTABLE *takes* LOOPHOLE *and* QUACK *each by the arm.*)

CONSTABLE: Come along. 'Pears as if the police in a couple of towns are lookin' for you fellows.

LOOPHOLE: Curses! (*Shaking fist at* ABNER) But I'll have my revenge.

ABNER: I wouldn't be placin' any bets on that. (CONSTABLE, LOOPHOLE, *and* QUACK *exit.*)

ELIZA: Mercy me—what a day!

GRISELDA: It's wonderful.

GLORY (*Icily*): You still have left a good many things un-explained, Abner Crane.

ABNER: Oh, you mean about Fifi LaTour.

ELIZA: Yes, must be quite a story there, Abner.

ABNER: I was able to explain everything to Constable Perkins. Fact is, I didn't trust that girl from the beginnin'. Too painted up she was. My paw used to say, "Abner, never trust a coat of paint. You can't ever be sure what's under it."

ELIZA: Wise words.

ABNER: So I set out to test her. Told her I had eight

hundred dollars on me. Fact is, I wouldn't be so foolish as to carry cash on me. But I was carryin' a whole bunch of cigar coupons—been savin' 'em up toward a new churn. She took 'em from my pocket, and I told the Constable what he'd find in her pocket. She planted her own purse on me. When the Constable saw the cigar coupons in her pocket, like I said, he knew right away how things were.

GLORY (*Melting*): Oh, Abner, you're so clever.

ABNER: And all that kissin' and stuff—well, she was doin' it, not me. Fair to have broke my neck.

ELIZA: Well, Abner, you sure gave me a turn for a while, but I'm glad everything is all settled now. I'm goin' to take this nice money into the kitchen and count it to my heart's content. (*She exits with money.* GRISELDA *follows her off.*)

GLORY (*Going to* ABNER): I'm sorry, Abner, for misjudging you.

ABNER (*Shyly*): Shucks, anybody can make a mistake.

GLORY: I was cruel.

ABNER: Don't pay it no mind.

GLORY: And now Mother has sold the farm and has five thousand dollars.

ABNER: That's nice.

GLORY: And I'm wondering about my own future.

ABNER: You can always help to spend the five thousand. Sounds like a mighty pleasant chore.

GLORY: I always like a man to help me with my chores.

ABNER: Well, they say I'm mighty handy. (*Bashfully*) I'll try to be useful.

GLORY: That's wonderful, Abner. (*Dreamily*) Sometimes I wish you were more—well, romantic. Loophole always talked so beautifully of moonlight, soft music and flowers.

ABNER (*Coming toward her*): Anyone can *talk* about flowers—
but actions speak louder than words. (*He takes a small
object* * *from his pocket, holds it up and presses it. A big bunch
of flowers springs out and he presents it to the ecstatic* GLORY.
ABNER *smiles broadly at* GLORY *as the curtains close.*)

THE END

*This bunch of "Spring Flowers" may be purchased at a magician supply
house; or a small bouquet of artificial flowers may be substituted.

Production Notes

ABNER CRANE FROM HAYSEED LANE

Characters: 4 male; 5 female.

Playing Time: 30 minutes.

Costumes: Loophole wears a black suit, white shirt and flowing bow tie, typical of the late nineties. Others dress in costumes of the period: Glory, Eliza, and Griselda in long dresses and white aprons. Abner wears overalls, a blue shirt and a straw hat and a large watch in his pocket. Fifi LaTour wears a long, tight-fitting, slinky dress, long earrings, and a good deal of other jewelry to give the effect of gaudiness, and she carries a small purse. Quigley dresses in a style similar to Loophole's. Constable Perkins wears a blue suit, blue hat with visor, and a star-shaped badge on his jacket.

Properties: Basin, wooden spoon, mending basket, stockings, needle, thread, basin with cereal to represent chicken feed, broom, small purse, roll of coupons, cups and saucers, dustcloth, black bag, packages of stage money, large sheet of paper representing legal document, quill pen and ink-well, bunch of "Spring Flowers."

Setting: Scene 1: The living room of the Rhode farm furnished in typical Old New England farm style: Upstage center is a door leading to outside, and at left and right of this are windows. In the center stands a large table on which there are a vase with flowers and the family Bible. Downstage center there is a rocking chair and down-

211

stage left a rather shabby sofa. On the wall, left, there is a sampler which reads, "Home Sweet Home." Scenes 2 and 3 may be played in front of curtains. For Scene 3 a table and two chairs, suggesting a restaurant, should be in the center of the stage. Scene 4 is the same as Scene 1.

Lighting: No special effects.

The Face Is Familiar

Characters

JOEL BAXTER, *a good-looking young fellow of twenty*
HAROLD ROBBINS, *his friend*
WALLY PEARSON, *Joel's chubby roommate*
CELIA, *a pretty girl of nineteen*
MARIE, *Celia's attractive friend*
DEAN HARRISON BIGELOW, *a pompous little man*
COUSIN CLARICE, *a middle-aged woman of strong character*
STILLWATER STUDENTS, *five boys or more, if desired*

TIME: *An afternoon in May, 1895.*
SETTING: *The study of Joel Baxter's dormitory rooms at Stillwater College.*
AT RISE: JOEL BAXTER *is placing a tray of sandwiches on the small serving table beside the desk at right.* HAROLD ROBBINS *is patting and fluffing a couple of pillows on sofa at downstage left.*

HAROLD: You know, Joel, I feel like a blooming housewife. Don't you think I've got the true domestic touch?
JOEL: Don't complain, Harold. It's all for a good cause. (*Standing off and inspecting tray of sandwiches*) There. Those

sandwiches look really appetizing. They add just the right note of dignity and charm to the occasion.

HAROLD (*Coming to serving table*): Say, they do look inviting, don't they? And I'm starved. (*He reaches for a sandwich, but* JOEL *smacks his arm.*)

JOEL: Keep away from the goodies, you wolf! Those are for the girls.

HAROLD: Hang the girls. You know that females nowadays don't eat—they just nibble. Heck, they don't have *room* for food. They all but disappear at the waistline! (*Describes hourglass figure with his hands*)

JOEL: Well, you might at least leave them something to nibble on.

HAROLD (*Reluctantly leaves sandwiches, goes to sofa at downstage left, sits*): Where's that daffy roommate of yours?

JOEL: You mean Wally Pearson?

HAROLD: Yes, good old Wally.

JOEL: He'll be back soon, I know that. Wherever there's food, Wally is, too. And he can smell out vittles from fifty miles away.

HAROLD (*Leaning back and clasping hands behind his neck*): I feel a bit nervous. After all, I've never met Marie Sadler.

JOEL: You'll like her. (*Dreamily*) She's almost as pretty as Celia.

HAROLD: Ah, Celia. (*Elaborating*) The Rose of Sharon, Helen of Troy, Cleopatra, a touch of Elaine . . .

JOEL (*Warmly*): You bet she is—and better than all of them.

HAROLD: Are you really going to propose to her this afternoon?

JOEL (*Pacing the floor somewhat nervously*): Well . . . if my voice and nerve hold out, I will. Anyway, I want you around here for moral support. You and Cousin Clarice, that is.

HAROLD: Cousin Clarice. That sounds formidable—what's she look like?

JOEL: To tell you the truth, I haven't seen her since I was a boy. She's been living in Europe and only recently returned to this country. She's a tough old bird, as I remember her, with the temper of a Bengal tiger.

HAROLD: Sounds real appealing. But why are you having her down here today?

JOEL: She's been wanting to come and see me, anyway—so I'm really killing two birds with one stone.

HAROLD (*Puzzled*): Is your Cousin Clarice one of the birds? (JOEL *goes to table at center and takes a small pamphlet from it.*)

JOEL (*Opening pamphlet*): Listen, and all will be as clear as crystal. I shall now read from that soul-stirring document entitled, "Rules and Regulations concerning the Conduct of the Gentlemanly Students of Stillwater College."

HAROLD: Hear! Hear!

JOEL: No remarks, please. Just lend me your ears. (*He reads aloud.*) "If a young gentleman wishes, in the interest of friendship and social pleasure, to entertain a young lady in his rooms, he must arrange for the presence of a respectable female chaperon of mature years. The college does not frown on friendship between the sexes, but such friendships must be carried on within the bounds of decorum. Extreme penalties are provided for the violation of this rule."

HAROLD: I begin to see the light. Cousin Clarice is to be the "chaperon of mature years."

JOEL: Exactly. When she accepted my invitation, I invited Celia and Marie for the afternoon. I wanted Celia to see me in these intellectual surroundings. She can't fail to be impressed. Look at all those books— (*Gestures toward bookcase*) I had to borrow at least three dozen of them.

HAROLD (*Incredulously*): Books? To *impress* her with?

JOEL (*Shyly*): Celia thinks a man should be intellectual.

HAROLD: That rule about chaperons sounds old hat to me. Golly, you'd think that in this enlightened year of 1895, a college student would be allowed more freedom.

JOEL: Don't be a radical, Harold. We have to follow the rules. And Celia wouldn't have it otherwise. She's a stickler for decorum.

HAROLD: She sounds a little stuffy, if you ask me.

JOEL (*Hotly*): Celia is *not* stuffy. She's just well brought up. She's beautiful, wonderful, and—

HAROLD: All right. Forget I said anything. But I just hope Marie doesn't like books that well.

JOEL: Dean Bigelow is sure to look in at some time during the afternoon, so we really have to have a chaperon.

HAROLD: Good old "Snoopy" Bigelow. The college watch-dog. (WALLY PEARSON *enters at center, carrying a large suit box under one arm and a telegram in his other hand. He is out of breath.*)

WALLY: Hello, friends. (*Hands telegram to* JOEL.) This just came for you.

HAROLD: What are you all out of breath for, Wally? You sound like an anemic steam engine.

WALLY: I want to try on this costume. It's a beauty.

HAROLD: Costume?

WALLY: It's for tonight's masquerade party over at the club. Look. (*He places box on sofa, opens it, and holds up a wig of graying brown, a long black skirt, a shirtwaist, and a voluminous black shawl. He puts the skirt on over his trousers and the wig on his head.*)

HAROLD: You're actually going to wear that rig?

WALLY: Sure. I'll be the belle of the ball. I'm going to do a number with some of the other boys.

JOEL (*Reading telegram*): Oh, golly!

WALLY (*Gathering up rest of costume and going toward bedroom door, right*): I'm going to don the rest of these glad rags. You birds are in for the treat of your young lives. (*He exits right.*)

JOEL (*Opening telegram and reading it to himself*): I'm ruined!

HAROLD: Don't be so faint of heart, Joel. Wally may prove to be another Cleopatra in that outfit.

JOEL: It's not that dizzy Wally that's bothering me. It's this. Read it and weep. (*Hands telegram to* HAROLD)

HAROLD (*Reading aloud*): "Unable to come today. Delayed by business matters in Boston. Will see you one week from today. Sorry for the delay. Love, Cousin Clarice."

JOEL: And the girls will be here at any moment.

HAROLD: A grim situation.

JOEL: Grim! It's a catastrophe. Celia is a high-minded girl —bless her heart. She won't step a foot inside this room without a chaperon present. And, besides, if Dean Bigelow comes snooping around—and he's sure to—I'd be expelled on the spot if the girls are here and Cousin Clarice isn't.

HAROLD: Can't you get another chaperon?

JOEL: They don't grow on trees, you know. And my acquaintance with elderly ladies is limited, to say the least.

HAROLD: Well, postpone the afternoon's festivities.

JOEL: But don't you understand. I've been working up my nerve all week for this occasion. This was to be the great day of my life. I was going to propose to Celia. She'd blush, and say yes, and I'd be the happiest man in the world.

HAROLD: Maybe you've had a narrow escape and don't know it.

JOEL: Don't be such a cynic, Harold. Have you no conception of what true love is? (WALLY *suddenly appears in doorway. He is now wearing the long, black skirt, the wig, the shirtwaist, and the shawl.*)

WALLY (*In high-pitched voice*): Speaking of true love, my dears, isn't this rig a beaut?

HAROLD: Holy mackerel! You'll set the female sex back fifty years.

WALLY (*Coming to center and turning around coquettishly to show off his costume*): Fetching, eh? If I don't win first prize at the masquerade, the judges are crooked, blind or crazy.

HAROLD: Well, don't expect Joel to appreciate your feminine beauty. He's just received a great shock.

JOEL (*Dismally*): Cousin Clarice can't come.

WALLY: So the old girl has stood you up, hey? Tough luck. No Clarice, no chaperon. (*Struts over to center door and looks out*) Some costume, hey? Whoops! The girls are on the way. They're coming up the walk. Say, they're pretty.

JOEL (*Rushes to door and looks out*): Oh, golly, we're sunk!

HAROLD: Wait—all is not lost. We have a potential chaperon in our midst. (*WALLY has strutted back to center. His back is to JOEL and HAROLD.*)

JOEL (*Pointing to WALLY's back*): You mean—?

HAROLD: Why not? (*Both creep up softly to WALLY, and each grabs one of WALLY's arms.*)

JOEL (*Coaxingly*): Wally, you and I are great friends, aren't we?

WALLY: True blue, old boy, true blue.

JOEL: Then I know you'll do me a favor that will just about save my life.

HAROLD: Of course he will.

WALLY (*Struggling in their grasp*): Now wait a minute—I don't like the sound of this.

JOEL: Wally, you've got to be Cousin Clarice.

WALLY (*Horrified*): Not on your life. What do you think I am?

HAROLD: True blue, that's what you are. Everybody says so.

WALLY: Then everybody is off his head! (*He breaks away from them and goes toward bedroom door right. JOEL and HAROLD chase him. JOEL tackles him as WALLY gets to door. JOEL and HAROLD sit on WALLY, whose skirt is up revealing the trousers underneath.*) Let me up!

JOEL: Please, Wally. We don't have much time. You've got to get us out of this jam. It'll just be for a little while. We'll pay you for it.

WALLY: How?

JOEL: I'll buy you the biggest steak dinner you've ever seen at McNamara's Steak House.

WALLY (*Weakening*): Steak?

HAROLD: Three inches thick.

WALLY: With mushrooms?

JOEL: All the mushrooms you can eat. Also onions.

WALLY: And Delmonico potatoes?

JOEL: A ton of them.

WALLY: You promise on your honor as a Stillwater senior?

JOEL: I solemnly promise. (*Girls' voices are heard from offstage. There is a knock at the door, followed by a pleasant female voice saying, "Anyone at home?" JOEL and HAROLD begin to rise quickly.*)

JOEL: You'll do it then, Wally?

WALLY: I suppose so. (*Grinning*) It might be fun at that—and a steak's a steak. (WALLY *is just rising with some difficulty from the floor when the center door opens, and* CELIA *and* MARIE *appear at center doorway.* WALLY *catches sight of them and rushes out of room through right exit as girls come to center.*)

CELIA: Is everyone deaf? I took the liberty of coming in. (*She has noted* WALLY's *swift exit.*) What's wrong, and who was that?

JOEL (*Uncomfortably*): How nice to see you, Celia—and you, too, Marie. That—that was Cousin Clarice.

CELIA (*Coming to center with* MARIE *and smiling*): Oh, yes. Our chaperon. (*Frowning*) But I thought I saw her rising from the floor—

MARIE: So did I. Has anything happened?

HAROLD (*Quickly*): She was a little overcome at seeing Joel after so many years.

JOEL: Y-yes, that's it. She felt somewhat faint.

MARIE (*Teasingly*): My, what an effect you have on the ladies!

CELIA (*Going toward bedroom door*): Poor old thing. Perhaps I had better see if she is all right.

JOEL (*Blocking her way*): No, no—please don't. She'll be fine—and, besides, she's a bit shy with strangers.

HAROLD: Yes, she's a regular shrinking violet.

JOEL (*Changing subject*): Oh, before I forget, Celia, you know Harold, of course.

CELIA: Of course.

JOEL: And Marie, this is Harold Robbins. Miss Sadler— Mr. Robbins.

HAROLD (*Holding out his hand*): How do you do, Miss Sadler. (*They shake hands, and* HAROLD *looks at her appreciatively.*) I can see that all Joel has said about you is true.

CELIA (*Teasingly*): Aha! Joel Baxter, what have you been saying about other girls?

HAROLD: Only that Miss Sadler is pretty and charming.

MARIE (*Dropping a little curtsey*): Oh, thank you, Joel. And thank you, Mr. Robbins.

JOEL: Why don't you girls sit down? (CELIA *and* MARIE *go to sofa where they sit.*)

CELIA: How pleasant your rooms are, Joel.

JOEL: Oh, thank you. (*He looks anxiously toward bedroom.*) I think I had better look in on Cousin Clarice.

CELIA: Yes, do. And be sure to call me if I can help in any way. (JOEL *goes to bedroom door and knocks.*)

JOEL: Are you feeling better, Cousin Clarice? (*Very loudly*) I have told the girls about your brief fainting spell! (*The door opens, and* WALLY *appears in the doorway. He speaks in high-pitched voice while playing role of* CLARICE.)

WALLY: Thank you, Joel, dear—I am feeling quite fit now.

JOEL: I'm glad to hear it. Let me help you to a chair.

WALLY: You dear boy, you're so thoughtful!

CELIA (*Coming to them*): Let me help, too. (*She and* JOEL *take* WALLY *by each arm and guide him to chair at left of table.*)

WALLY: You must be Celia. My, what a pretty creature you are. I don't blame dear Joel for his warm feelings toward you.

CELIA: Thank you, Miss—

WALLY: Call me Cousin Clarice.

CELIA: I will. Thank you, Cousin Clarice. (WALLY *sits down.*)

WALLY: Both of you have been so helpful. (*To* CELIA) Come here closer, my dear. I should like to give you an affectionate kiss. (CELIA *comes to* WALLY, *who kisses her solidly on the cheek.*) You're a dear, sweet girl. (JOEL, *standing behind* WALLY, *gives him a poke in the shoulder and looks exasperated.*) Ouch, stupe!

MARIE: What was that about stupe?

JOEL (*Hurriedly*): Not stupe—soup. Cousin Clarice is very fond of ox-tail soup. I promised I'd see that she gets some for dinner tonight.

WALLY (*Looking toward* MARIE): And who is this dear child?

JOEL: Oh, I'm sorry. I forgot you hadn't met Marie. Marie Sadler—Cousin Clarice.

WALLY: I'm delighted to meet you, my child. My, how pretty the young girls are nowadays. Come here, my dear—and let me look at you. (MARIE *rises and comes to* WALLY.) Mmm—a lovely peaches and cream complexion. I should like to give you an affectionate kiss. (*He does so.*)

HAROLD: Say, what is this!

CELIA: Don't be rude, Mr. Robbins. I think Cousin Clarice is just as sweet as sugar.

WALLY: Thank you, my dear. (*He rises and hugs* CELIA. JOEL *again pokes him.*) And you, too, my dear. (*He hugs* MARIE *also.*) Ah, youth, youth! (CELIA *and* MARIE *each kiss him on the cheek.*)

JOEL (*Trying to break this up*): Why don't we walk for a while in the garden? It's such a lovely day.

MARIE: A good idea. The air is like wine.

HAROLD (*Coming to her and offering his arm*): Shall we?

MARIE: Of course, Mr. Robbins. We'll see you anon, Cousin Clarice.

WALLY: I shall count the moments, my dear. (*He pinches her cheek playfully before she and* HAROLD *exit center.*)

JOEL (*Taking* WALLY'S *arm and obviously pinching it*): Why don't you just rest here for a few moments, Cousin Clarice?

WALLY: I'm not at all tired. (JOEL *increases the pressure.*) Ouch. All right. All right!

JOEL (*Quickly*): Cousin Clarice sometimes overestimates her strength. Ladies at her age should nap a little in the afternoon.

CELIA: Yes, Cousin Clarice, you just sit here and rest. (*She helps* WALLY *into chair*.) Let me make you comfortable. (*She straightens* WALLY'S *shawl*.) Now, isn't that nice.

WALLY (*Taking her hand*): You're so good to a bothersome old lady.

CELIA: You're not bothersome at all. You're sweet. (*She again kisses* WALLY'S *cheek, and* WALLY *hugs her*.) Coming, Joel?

JOEL: You go ahead, Celia. I'll join you in a moment. We'll probably have a bite to eat when we come in, and I'd like to make sure that things are in order.

CELIA: Very well. Don't be long. (*She goes to center door*.)

JOEL: I won't be. (CELIA *exits*.)

WALLY (*In natural voice*): She's a dream!

JOEL (*Angrily*): Look here, I know you're doing me a favor and all that, but is it absolutely necessary for you to kiss and hug the girls incessantly?

WALLY: Control yourself, old boy, control yourself! I'm just playing my part.

JOEL: And to the hilt. I never saw anyone so enjoy a role in all my life. And please be careful. Before you know it, the girls will become suspicious.

WALLY: Then stop smacking me when I'm only doing my duty. My shoulders and arms must be black and blue.

JOEL: And don't forget that Dean Bigelow probably will be dropping in. For heaven's sake, behave like a lady if he does.

WALLY: Old Snoopy himself? Does he know I'm here?

JOEL: He knows my Cousin Clarice is supposed to be here. He asked all sorts of questions about her. When I told him she was wealthy and unmarried, his eyes lit up like a comet. I also told him she had a violent temper, but that didn't seem to bother him.

WALLY: Cousin Clarice has a violent temper?

JOEL: Strong men shudder and children quail when she cuts loose.

WALLY: Mmm. Very interesting.

JOEL: Now don't go getting any lunatic ideas.

WALLY: Have no fear, my boy. Have no fear. (*He rises and moves toward bedroom.*) I think I'll have a cigar to give me strength. (JOEL *grabs him and pushes him back into the chair.*)

JOEL: Leave the cigars alone! If anyone smells them on your breath, we're done for!

WALLY: Well, if you want to deprive a sweet old lady of the simple pleasures of life.

JOEL: Just sit there and be calm. I've other business to attend to.

WALLY: And nice business, too. I wouldn't mind being in your shoes myself. Though why Celia should want to throw away her life on you, I'll never know.

JOEL: Don't let it bother you. Just continue the way you are. And try to act like a lady.

WALLY (*In falsetto*): Goodbye, dear cousin. (JOEL *goes to center door.*)

JOEL: Remember now—behave! (JOEL *exits.* WALLY *rises, goes to sofa, and lies down with his knees in the air. He begins to sing raucously* "Drink to Me Only with Thine Eyes." *There is a sudden knock at center door.* WALLY *jumps up, straightens his skirt, and sits in a ladylike position on the sofa.*)

WALLY (*Sweetly, in falsetto again*): Come in. (DEAN HARRISON BIGELOW *enters.*)

DEAN: I trust I am not intruding.

WALLY (*Rather ferociously*): If you're a burglar, I'll tear you apart.

DEAN (*Somewhat taken aback*): I am Dean Harrison Bigelow of Stillwater College.

WALLY: Oh, I beg your pardon, Dean. You look just like a pickpocket I once saw.

DEAN (*Coughing*): Er—yes. Where are the young people?

WALLY: They are in the garden. The day is so lovely.

DEAN: How true! (*Comes to sofa and holds out his hand*) You must be Mr. Baxter's cousin. (WALLY *grips the* DEAN'S *hand, and he winces.*)

WALLY: Yes, I am Cousin Clarice.

DEAN: May I sit down?

WALLY: Go right ahead, Dean. (DEAN *sits.*) Wally has spoken so much about you. (*Coquettishly*) You are quite a hero to all the boys. They admire you so.

DEAN (*Swelling*): Do they, indeed?

WALLY (*Pulls lace handkerchief out of skirt pocket, gestures coquettishly with it as he speaks*): Oh, yes. Joel was just remarking, "Now if only Dean Bigelow would come, our day would be complete."

DEAN: A splendid fellow, young Joel—splendid!

WALLY (*Still waving handkerchief*): And his roommate, young Wallace Pearson—what an appealing young man! So kind, so witty, so genuinely helpful.

DEAN (*Dubiously*): Wallace Pearson?

WALLY (*With an ecstatic wave of the handkerchief*): Yes, and *such* a gentleman! I admire true gentlemen with all my heart. (*Unknowingly drops handkerchief*)

DEAN (*Noticing handkerchief on floor, dropping to his hands and knees to pick it up*): Ah, then let *me* be a gentleman, my dear lady.

WALLY (*Eyes closed, hands clasped, continues extravagant praise, oblivious of* DEAN): His thoughtfulness has warmed my heart—he has a soul, that boy. You can see it in his eyes. (WALLY *rises to his feet in his enthusiasm and unknowingly steps on* DEAN'S *hand, which is extended toward handkerchief.* DEAN *winces visibly and tries to extricate hand without attracting* WALLY'S *attention.*) His eyes are luminous with the true generosity of his spirit, the goodness of his heart, the quickness of his mind. (DEAN, *still on hands and knees, tugs unsuccessfully to free his hand, grimacing.*) Not just native ability, you understand, but zealous industry as well. The devil may find work for idle hands, but not for the hands of young Wallace Pearson. (DEAN *struggles desperately. Finally, with hesitation and deference, he plucks at hem of* WALLY'S *skirt.*)

DEAN (*Pleadingly*): Ah, Madam—

WALLY (*Still oblivious*): The profundity of his observations, the lilt and sparkle of his words . . . (DEAN, *with enormous effort, finally reaches the handkerchief with his free hand, holds it up.*)

DEAN: Madam!

WALLY: Yes, Dean?

DEAN (*Exhausted, holds up handkerchief*): Your handkerchief, Madam. (WALLY *takes handkerchief, releases* DEAN'S *hand, still unaware that he has ever stepped on it.* DEAN *rises to his feet, much relieved, nursing hand.*)

WALLY: Why, thank you, Dean. You are indeed a true gentleman. (DEAN *looks aside bashfully.*) And I am considered an expert judge of character even though I did mistake you for a pickpocket when you first entered. (*Giggles coquettishly*) Since then, of course, I have revised my original estimate of you. Now I can sense the integrity and appeal of your personality.

DEAN (*Eagerly*): You can?

WALLY: It is as though the sunlight has streamed into the room.

DEAN: Bless my soul. You are very astute, indeed. (*Moving*

closer to WALLY) And I might say that I, too, from the moment I entered, have been most favorably impressed.

WALLY (*Slapping at him playfully*): Oh, Dean!

DEAN: Most impressed. I sensed that you, too, are a woman of character.

WALLY (*Again slapping at him*): You naughty man!

DEAN: Joel tells me you come originally from Boston.

WALLY: Yes, the land of the bean and the home of the cod.

DEAN: And of charming ladies, if I may say so.

WALLY (*Coquettishly*): You may.

DEAN: You have been living in Europe?

WALLY: Yes, but I had to return. I have vast properties to look after in Boston.

DEAN (*Coming still closer*): Vast properties?

WALLY (*Swinging out his arms and hitting the* DEAN *on the chest*): This vast! Oh, excuse me. I have a dreadful habit of talking with my hands.

DEAN (*Coughing violently*): That is quite all right. (*Rising*) May I ask a bold question?

WALLY (*Demurely*): Oh, sir, if it is not too bold.

DEAN: Would you do me the honor of walking in the garden with me?

WALLY: Why, yes. That would be nice. (WALLY *rises, the* DEAN *takes his arm, and they exit center.* WALLY *kicks his skirt awkwardly just as they exit. After a moment or two,* JOEL *and* CELIA *enter at center.*)

JOEL: Alone at last.

CELIA: Yes, the garden is becoming quite crowded. Who is that pompous little man who seems to have taken such a fancy to Cousin Clarice?

JOEL: That's Dean Bigelow. But let's not talk about him. (*Nervously*) Y-y-know, Celia, there has been something of great importance on my mind.

CELIA: Some college matter, I suppose. I imagine you must be studying very hard.

JOEL: N-no. I mean y-yes. I have been studying hard. But that's not what I mean.

CELIA: I hope you're not worried about the sandwiches. (*Going to serving table*) They look most edible.

JOEL: Hang the sandwiches!

CELIA: Why, Joel!

JOEL: I'm sorry. I didn't mean to sound sharp.

CELIA: I'm beginning to believe you really are worried about something. (*She walks back toward center, and* JOEL *follows her.*)

JOEL: I am worried, but it's a sort of pleasant worry.

CELIA: Goodness, that sounds contradictory.

JOEL: Oh, gosh, Celia, I'm not very good at pretty speeches, and a pretty speech is what I need right now. (*He goes down on one knee.*) C-Celia, I— (*Suddenly blurting it out*) I have the honor of asking—of asking for your hand in marriage. (*Just as he concludes his speech,* WALLY *rushes in at center, closely pursued by the* DEAN. WALLY *knocks over* JOEL, *who is still on one knee.*)

WALLY: Oops! Sorry! (*The* DEAN *catches up to* WALLY, *who strikes him playfully across the chest.*) You naughty man! (*The* DEAN *giggles like a schoolgirl, and* WALLY *rushes out center, the* DEAN *still pursuing him.*)

JOEL (*Getting up*): Darn it! What a time for a relay race!

CELIA (*Smiling*): The answer is yes, Joel.

JOEL (*Delighted*): Yes!

CELIA: Oui, ja, yes—whatever language suits you.

JOEL (*Embracing her*): Oh, Celia. (MARIE *and* HAROLD *enter at center.*)

HAROLD: Now, now—let's observe decorum.

MARIE: How romantic.

HAROLD: You're Dean Bigelow's equal as a ladies' man. He and Cousin Clarice are playing hide-and-seek in the garden.

JOEL: You're looking at the happiest man in the world. Celia has consented to become my wife.

MARIE (*Embracing* CELIA): Oh, Celia, how wonderful.

HAROLD (*Shaking* JOEL's *hands*): Congratulations, Joel.

JOEL: Thank you. I'm a lucky fellow. (*Looking suddenly worried*) I'm afraid, though, we had better rescue Cousin Clarice from Dean Bigelow's clutches. I had no idea the old boy had so much life in him.

HAROLD: An excellent idea—one should always come to the aid of a damsel in distress.

CELIA: You boys go out; Marie and I will follow in a moment.

JOEL: Right. This is man's work, after all.

HAROLD: And we'll have some refreshment after the rescue. (*He and* HAROLD *exit quickly.*)

MARIE: Hasn't it been a wonderful afternoon—especially for you?

CELIA: Marvelous. But, Marie, does something strike you as peculiar around here?

MARIE: Peculiar?

CELIA: I'm referring to Cousin Clarice. Did you note a smell of tobacco on her breath?

MARIE: Why, yes, I did.

CELIA: And don't you note the way she walks? She doesn't walk like a woman. And, Marie, I'm almost positive that I caught a glimpse of trousers under her skirt when she was meandering through the garden.

MARIE: So did I. But I didn't want to say anything about it.

CELIA: In short, I have a suspicion Cousin Clarice is a man.

MARIE: Heavens!

CELIA (*Quickly*): But I'm sure there's some good reason for the masquerade. After all, I trust Joel implicitly. I know he is absolutely incapable of a mean or underhanded action.

MARIE: Of course.

CELIA: But to say that my womanly curiosity is aroused is almost an understatement. Let's do a bit of investigating.

MARIE: Let's. It ought to be fun. (*They exit center. The stage is empty for a moment. Then there is a knock at the door. The door then opens, and* COUSIN CLARICE *enters. She looks around and comes to center.*)

CLARICE: Is anybody about? (*She goes to bedroom door and looks in.*) Joel? Well, since the dear boy didn't expect me, I suppose he's out. At least I can make myself comfortable until his return. (*She selects a magazine from table at center, goes to sofa, sits down, and begins to browse through magazine.* WALLY *suddenly rushes through center door, with* DEAN BIGELOW *in pursuit.*)

WALLY: Really, Dean, you are a very naughty man!

DEAN: Ah, Clarice, you are enough to drive a man out of his wits! Come, my dear.

CLARICE (*Coughing*): Ahem!

DEAN: Oh, I beg your pardon, madam.

CLARICE: You ought to. Fine goings on in the room of a college dormitory.

WALLY: The Dean is so impetuous.

DEAN: I don't believe I have the pleasure of your acquaintance, madam.

CLARICE (*To* WALLY): Did you say Dean?

WALLY: I did.

CLARICE (*Rising from sofa*): Then you must be Dean Bigelow. I am Joel Baxter's Cousin Clarice.

DEAN: You're what!

CLARICE: Really, Dean Bigelow, are you accustomed to addressing the gentle sex in that raucous tone? I find it most ungentlemanly. (WALLY *has begun to edge toward bedroom door right.*)

DEAN: I beg your pardon, but I find this most bewildering. If you are Joel's Cousin Clarice, who is this? (*He turns to where* WALLY *has been standing, notes* WALLY *is no longer there, and then sees* WALLY *making for the bedroom.*) Stop! An explanation is in order. (*He rushes after* WALLY *and grabs* WALLY'S *arm just as* WALLY *reaches doorway.*)

WALLY: Ouch!

CLARICE: Sir, unhand that woman!

DEAN (*To* WALLY): Who are you? (JOEL, CELIA, HAROLD, *and* MARIE *enter at center.* JOEL, *catching sight of* COUSIN CLARICE, *stops dead in his tracks. His mouth drops open.*)

WALLY (*Seeing them*): You fellows got me into this mess— now get me out of it!

CLARICE: Joel, dear. (*She comes to him and kisses him on the cheek.*) How nice to see you after all these years.

JOEL: C-cousin Clarice.

HAROLD: Help!

CLARICE: I found after I sent the telegram that I could come after all. I was able to clear up my business more rapidly than I anticipated—so I thought I would come to Stillwater anyway and surprise you.

JOEL: You did!

CLARICE: But I seem to have intruded on some strange happenings. I found Dean Bigelow here in close pursuit of the strange woman standing yonder.

WALLY: I'm not strange, and I'm not a woman.

DEAN: Aha! So the truth will out! (*He grabs* WALLY'S *wig and pulls it off.*) So—Wallace Pearson! Your days at Stillwater are numbered!

WALLY: Let me explain, Dean—let me explain.

DEAN (*To* JOEL): You realize, Mr. Baxter, the consequences of this horrendous deception. You are familiar, of course, with the rules governing the conduct of the gentleman students of Stillwater College. (*To* MARIE *and* CELIA) In the name of the college, I wish to apologize to you young ladies for the fraud that has been perpetrated upon you.

CELIA: No apology is necessary. We have known for some time now that Wally was not Cousin Clarice.

MARIE: Of course we have.

DEAN: That does not speak well for your sense of decorum. Knowing the truth, you persisted in staying on—against college regulations.

CELIA (*Spiritedly*): Yes, we did. We knew no harm was intended and that my fiancé must have had good reason for what he did.

DEAN: Hmmph. Your fiancé, indeed! Well, let me tell you, your prospective husband will marry you minus a degree from Stillwater College. We must preserve decorum.

CLARICE (*Acidly*): Now, see here, Dean Bigelow, it strikes me that your own conduct, as I witnessed it not five minutes ago in this room, is scarcely a model of propriety.

WALLY: You tell him, Cousin. I've probably weakened my heart running away from him all afternoon.

DEAN: It is not my conduct that is in question. It is that of your nephew and his iniquitous roommate.

CLARICE (*Sweetly*): Do you happen to know Dudley Murgatroyd?

DEAN: Of course—he is the chairman of the Board of Trustees of Stillwater College.

CLARICE: He is also one of my most intimate friends. I have a suspicion that if I told him of your carryings-on here this afternoon, Stillwater College might be looking for a new dean.

DEAN (*Startled*): Let us not be hasty.

CLARICE: Exactly what I advise. I feel that this entire situation here today is really my fault. What Joel has done is really quite innocent, anyway—after all, no harm has come of it. And do not forget that he actually has broken no rule, anyway, since I am now here and I am quite capable of serving as chaperon.

JOEL: Believe me, Dean, I meant no harm at all; I merely wanted the opportunity to ask Celia to become my wife.

CLARICE: So, under the circumstances, I do not think, Dean Bigelow, that you will take any disciplinary action against either Joel or Wally. (*Firmly*) What do you think?

DEAN: I—I—

CLARICE: And I know Dudley Murgatroyd would agree.

DEAN (*Quickly*): I—I think you are right.

CLARICE: Splendid.

DEAN: And I shall now take my leave. (*He glares at* WALLY *and then at* JOEL.) Good day—all. (*He exits center.*)

WALLY: Good day—sir.

JOEL (*Hugging* CLARICE): Cousin Clarice, you're wonderful.

CELIA (*Kissing her*): You're marvelous!

WALLY: And I'm tired!

HAROLD: Why don't we have a bite to eat now. There are sandwiches—and, Wally, fetch the lemonade. (WALLY *exits right.*)

MARIE: This has been the most interesting afternoon of my life—to say the least.

JOEL: And the happiest of mine. (*Squeezes* CELIA'S *hand*)

HAROLD: There's nothing like a quiet afternoon at Stillwater College to calm the nerves and ease the mind.

CELIA: And I think Wally was wonderful to do what he did for a friend. (WALLY *enters with large pitcher of lemonade.*)

WALLY: True blue, that's what I am!

JOEL: I'll get the glasses. (*He exits right.*)

CELIA (*Kissing* WALLY): Thank you for your great courage.

MARIE (*Also kissing him*): And your wonderful loyalty.

CLARICE (*Also kissing him*): And your gallant impersonation. (JOEL *enters with tray of glasses.*)

WALLY (*To* JOEL): The best part of being Cousin Clarice is the marks of gratitude that follow.

JOEL: Pour for all, Wally. (WALLY *fills the glasses, and each takes one.* WALLY *sets pitcher on serving table.*)

HAROLD: I now propose two toasts. First, to the newly affianced couple. (*All drink, except* JOEL *and* CELIA, *who smile happily.*) And second, to Cousin Clarice—in fact, to both Cousins Clarice, without whom Stillwater would be minus a couple of students.

CLARICE: That is sweet of you.

WALLY: You touch me, old man, you touch me.

HAROLD (*Raising glass*): To both Clarices. (*All drink.*)

JOEL: And on this, the happiest day of my life, may I venture a fond wish—I hope that never again will I have to endure the anguish of watching a muscular male masquerade as a woman.

HAROLD: Amen to that.

CLARICE: And now, let's have the quiet afternoon we planned. (*The center door suddenly bursts open, and in flock five young men dressed in female costume. One is disguised as a ballerina, two are dressed in flowing Grecian robes, the other two in conventional women's attire.*)

1ST STUDENT: Hi, Wally. Say, you look great. We thought we'd come over before the masquerade so that we could rehearse our number.

WALLY: Hey, that's a great idea!

JOEL: Ye gods! (WALLY *and his five friends line up in a row at center and begin a chorus-line dance, singing "In the Good Old Summertime." The dance becomes wilder and wilder, the singing becomes more and more raucous and less tuneful as the others clasp their hands over their ears, and the curtain falls.*)

THE END

Production Notes

THE FACE IS FAMILIAR

Characters: 9 male; 3 female; male extras for students, if
desired.

Playing Time: 35 minutes.

Costumes: Joel, Harold, and Wally wear the typical male
attire of the nineties: striped blazers, straw hats, etc.
Wally puts on long black skirt, wig, shirtwaist and shawl.
Celia and Marie wear long pastel gowns, bonnets, and
carry parasols. Dean Bigelow wears a dark suit, vest,
stiff collar and old-fashioned tie. Cousin Clarice wears
a long skirt, shirtwaist, shawl and bonnet; her clothes
should not be of the same colors as Wally's masquerade
costume. She carries a large dark umbrella. The Stillwater students enter dressed in female attire; one is
dressed as a ballerina, two wear flowing Grecian robes,
the other two may wear costumes similar to Wally's.

Properties: A tray of sandwiches, pitcher of lemonade, 6
glasses, telegram, box for Wally's costume, handkerchief.

Setting: The study of Joel Baxter's dormitory rooms at Stillwater College. There are two exits: The exit at upstage
center leads out to the garden; the exit at right leads to
the bedroom of the suite. At center is a table on which are
books, magazines, and a newspaper. At left and right of
this table are chairs. At downstage right is a desk with
chair and beside it is a small serving table which holds a
tray of sandwiches. At downstage left is a shabby but

comfortable sofa. To the right of the center exit is a fireplace, with a colorful banner above it, reading: "Stillwater College." To the left of center doorway is an amply stocked bookcase. On other walls, there may be pennants of other well-known colleges.

Lighting: No special effects.

What Ho!

Characters

LADY LETITIA HIGHTONE, *a domineering woman with a will of iron*
SIR HILARY HIGHTONE, *her absent-minded husband*
REGGIE HIGHTONE, *their son*
DIANA HIGHTONE, *their daughter, a pretty girl of twenty*
LADY CLARA CROWBAR, *Sir Hilary's romantic sister*
CLOVERBLOOM, *the butler*
HUMPHREY WITHERSPOON, *Sir Hilary's secretary*
DAVID DAUNTLESS, *a handsome American in his twenties*
MR. HARVEY DAUNTLESS, *David's good-natured father*
MRS. DAUNTLESS, *David's mother*

TIME: *One morning.*
SETTING: *The terrace of Sir Hilary Hightone's country home in England.*
AT RISE: SIR HILARY HIGHTONE *is seated at table at center of stage;* LADY HIGHTONE *sits opposite him. On the sidetable, at left of center door, are various covered dishes.* CLOVERBLOOM *stands at stiff and solemn attention beside this sidetable.*

LADY HIGHTONE: The kippers were excellent this morning, Cloverbloom.

CLOVERBLOOM: Thank you, m'lady.

SIR HILARY (*Blinking, in a mental fog as usual*): Kippers? Oh, yes, kippers. Dashed good, Cloverbloom, dashed good!

CLOVERBLOOM: Thank you, m'lord.

SIR HILARY (*Looking about near-sightedly*): Tea. I should have my tea. Where is my tea?

CLOVERBLOOM (*Patiently*): It is on the table before you, m'lord.

SIR HILARY: Tea? Table? (*He picks up cup.*) Why, bless my soul, so it is. Capital stuff. Capital.

LADY HIGHTONE: Clara is late for breakfast this morning.

SIR HILARY (*Vacantly*): Clara? (*He shakes his head.*) Who is Clara?

LADY HIGHTONE: Oh, Hilary, you're so vague. Lady Clara Crowbar. Your sister, Clara.

SIR HILARY (*Noisily sipping his tea*): Oh, Clara, to be sure. Fine woman. Fine woman. (*His wife glares at him.*)

LADY HIGHTONE: And don't slurp your tea so, Hilary. You sound like the *Queen Mary* coming into port.

SIR HILARY: Sorry, my dear.

CLOVERBLOOM: Lady Clara has already breakfasted, m'lady.

LADY HIGHTONE: Has she, indeed? It isn't like Clara to be up so early.

CLOVERBLOOM: She said something about going down to the village, m'lady.

LADY HIGHTONE (*Turning her attention back to her husband, who is still slurping happily*): As soon as you've finished your noisy tea-drinking, Hilary, you should go to your study and begin work. You simply must make better progress on the history of the family that you're writing.

SIR HILARY (*Blinking rapidly*): Dash it all, Letitia, I'm no writer. Hate the thought of sitting in the study on such a fine day. I ought to be out in the garden looking after the roses. Have to keep an eye on Angus, the gardener, you know.

LADY HIGHTONE (*Firmly*): You have to do no such thing. Angus is perfectly capable of looking after the garden himself. That's what he's paid for. And Mr. Witherspoon will be waiting for you in the study.

SIR HILARY: Witherspoon? Witherspoon? Never heard of him.

LADY HIGHTONE: Hilary, you're enough to drive anyone to the brink of insanity.

SIR HILARY (*Vaguely*): Thank you, my dear.

LADY HIGHTONE: Witherspoon! Humphrey Witherspoon! The Earl of Feefum's son. Your secretary, and certainly the most competent one you've ever had. And perhaps he'll be your son-in-law some day, if Diana ever comes to her senses.

SIR HILARY: Oh, that Witherspoon. Don't like the fellow. Never did. Don't want him for a son-in-law.

LADY HIGHTONE: Hilary, you're impossible! Finish your tea now, and then go to the study.

SIR HILARY: But it's such a deucedly fine day. I'd—

LADY HIGHTONE (*At her most commanding*): Hilary!

SIR HILARY (*Meekly putting down his cup at once*): Yes, my dear. Off at once. (*He rises and goes to center door where he bumps into his son,* REGGIE.)

REGGIE: Oops, Pater! Sorry and all that sort of rot. Beastly clumsy of me I know. I ask your paternal forgiveness.

SIR HILARY (*Coldly*): It'll be a happier world when you learn to look where you're going, Reggie.

REGGIE: I'll cover myself with sackcloth and ashes, old bean. Beastly sorry. I suppose you're off to work on the jolly old book. Well, pip, pip—I suppose you must be popping off.

Sir Hilary: Hmmph! (*He exits grumpily.*)

Reggie (*Going to sidetable*): And what have we here? Hmm . . . kippers, kidneys, shirred eggs, muffins. Bit too much for the old constitution today. About all I can assimilate is a cup of tea.

Cloverbloom: I'll get it for you, sir.

Reggie (*Coming to table*): Thanks, Cloverbloom, old bean. You're a prince of good fellows. (*He sits down.*) Well, Mater, jolly morning, what?

Lady Hightone (*Exasperated*): Reggie, I wish you wouldn't chatter so. I have a headache.

Reggie: Sorry, old thing. (Cloverbloom *pours tea for* Reggie.)

Lady Hightone: Have you seen your sister this morning?

Reggie: Looked out the old bedroom window an hour ago and saw her walking toward the river with that American chap, Dauntless.

Lady Hightone: There's obviously something between them.

Reggie: Well, they looked matey enough—walking hand in hand and all that. After all, Diana did rescue this Dauntless bloke from the jaws of death. That sort of thing creates a bond between a man and a woman.

Lady Hightone: Stuff and nonsense! All she did was find him with a badly sprained ankle on the road. He couldn't walk, so out of the goodness of her heart, she brought him here. And he's been with us for two weeks.

Reggie: His ankle's improving, though. He walks with a cane now. Fine fellow, Dauntless—full of beans and fun. I like him.

Lady Hightone: Well, I don't. And I don't approve of this obviously ripening friendship between Diana and him. After all, he's a common American.

REGGIE: What's wrong with Americans? Make the wheels of the world spin, don't they? I've known some frightfully interesting American chaps.

LADY HIGHTONE: Americans are all savages—loud, cheap, and pushing. The fact remains that this David Dauntless comes from some uncivilized place called Little Creek, Wyoming. And to cap it all, his family is in trade of some kind.

REGGIE: They own a dog food factory. After all, canines have to eat.

LADY HIGHTONE: Dog food. How revolting! He certainly is not a proper match for a girl who has the blood of the Crusaders in her. After all, we have our family to think of. You can't mix the Hightones with vulgar upstarts from Little Creek, Wyoming. And I have hopes that Diana and Humphrey Witherspoon will marry. He is an Earl's son.

REGGIE: Oh, well, no sense in crossing bridges before we come to them. This Dauntless chap will probably be leaving soon, anyway. He was on a walking tour, you know.

LADY HIGHTONE: He can't leave any too soon for me.

REGGIE: As for Witherspoon, he's a glum sort of bloke. Not my cup of tea at all. (LADY CLARA CROWBAR, *a plump, gushy type of woman enters.*)

LADY CLARA (*Somewhat breathless but cheerful*): Good morning, everyone!

REGGIE: 'Morning, Aunt Clara. Up with the birds today, weren't you?

LADY CLARA: I had a letter to post, and the day was so beautiful I decided to walk to the village.

LADY HIGHTONE: Walking two miles on a warm day is

scarcely the ideal occupation for a woman of your age, Clara.

LADY CLARA: Oh, bother my age! You're just as young as you feel, and I feel like a sixteen-year-old. And what I saw just now made me feel even younger.

REGGIE: Don't keep us in suspenders, as they say in the music halls, Aunt Clara. What did you see?

LADY CLARA: The most delightful sight! That handsome Dauntless young man and Diana were embracing.

LADY HIGHTONE (*Almost screaming*): Embracing!

LADY CLARA (*Happily*): It was really the most romantic sight. He kissed her tenderly, and she looked up at him as though he were a combination Greek god and cinema star. It was lovely!

REGGIE: Did they see you, old girl?

LADY CLARA: Of course not! You don't think I'd interrupt love's young dream, do you?

LADY HIGHTONE: This is positively frightful and completely disgusting! And this affair between Diana and the unspeakable Dauntless has gone quite far enough. We must put a stop to it, and Dauntless must leave! Imagine a Hightone consorting with a barbarian from Little Creek, Wyoming! It's an insult to the British Empire!

LADY CLARA: Oh, Letitia, you're just a spoil-sport! Young Dauntless is a very attractive and likeable young fellow. If I were twenty years younger, I'd set my cap for him myself.

LADY HIGHTONE (*Haughtily*): I trust you realize, Clara, that this likeable young fellow, as you call him, is an American whose family is engaged in trade. They manufacture dog food, of all things! Can you think of anything more common? It makes me shudder!

LADY CLARA: I'll wager there's money in dog food.

REGGIE: Hear! Hear!

LADY HIGHTONE: Need I remind you that the Hightones go back to the days of William the Conqueror? We have always been a proud family, and our marriages have remained in the proper circles. After all, one can't scoff at family and breeding.

LADY CLARA: What does Hilary think of all this?

LADY HIGHTONE (*With exasperation*): Have you ever known your brother Hilary to think for five minutes consecutively about anything? He hasn't the remotest notion of what has been going on. (DIANA HIGHTONE *and* DAVID DAUNTLESS *enter.* DAVID *limps slightly and walks with a cane.*)

DIANA (*Brightly*): Good morning, Mother. Good morning, Aunt Clara. Good morning, Reggie. Isn't it a perfect day?

AUNT CLARA (*Kittenishly*): Perfection is where you find it.

REGGIE: How's the ankle progressing, old boy?

DAVID: Very well, thanks. I'll be able to get rid of this cane pretty soon, I think.

LADY HIGHTONE (*Coldly*): Then you should be about ready to leave us, Mr. Dauntless.

DAVID (*Looking unhappily at* DIANA): Yes, I suppose I will. All of you have been very kind to me, and I want you to know I appreciate your hospitality.

REGGIE: Think nothing of it, old boy. Always glad to oblige.

LADY CLARA: It's been a pleasure to have you.

LADY HIGHTONE: And where will you go from here, Mr. Dauntless?

DAVID: Home, I think. This accident has upset my schedule. And Dad will need me in the factory.

LADY HIGHTONE (*Rather nastily*): Oh, yes, the factory. Dog food, isn't it?

DAVID: Yes, we call it Dauntless' Puppo. A bark in every bite.

REGGIE: Oh, I say, that's frightfully clever, David, old boy.

DAVID: Thanks, Reggie.

LADY HIGHTONE: I am going to be perfectly frank with you, Mr. Dauntless. I want you to leave this house as soon as possible.

DAVID (*Surprised*): Why, Lady Hightone, have I offended you in any way?

DIANA: Mother!

LADY HIGHTONE: Don't interrupt, Diana. I know exactly what has been going on. And I won't have it. No daughter of mine is going to ally herself with an American manufacturer of dog food. I won't have it—and that is that!

DAVID: Really, Lady Hightone, I feel you're being most unreasonable. My intentions toward Diana are perfectly honorable. I want to marry her.

LADY HIGHTONE: I can't think of any catastrophe that would be more ghastly than that!

DAVID: But Lady Hightone— (HUMPHREY WITHERSPOON, *Sir Hilary's secretary, enters suddenly, comes to center.*)

HUMPHREY (*Excitedly*): Lady Hightone, I have something of the gravest importance to tell you.

LADY HIGHTONE: Really, Humphrey, you arrive at a most inopportune time. I am dealing with this common American upstart.

DIANA: Mother, please!

HUMPHREY (*Disdainfully*): You mean Mr. Dauntless, of course.

LADY HIGHTONE: Naturally. I don't know of any other common American upstarts about the house.

HUMPHREY: He is not only common— (*Dramatically*) —he is also a thief.

DAVID: Look here, Witherspoon, you're just asking for a good punch in the jaw.

HUMPHREY (*Retreating somewhat*): Don't forget that I wear glasses.

LADY HIGHTONE: That will not hold him back, Humphrey. These upstart Americans have no code of either decency or honor.

HUMPHREY (*Taking a pearl necklace from his pocket*): Behold!

LADY HIGHTONE (*Grasping necklace*): My pearls!

LADY CLARA: What is all this, anyway?

REGGIE: I say, this is getting frightfully mysterious. Like a Sherlock Holmes story and all that sort of rot.

HUMPHREY: You may be interested to know that this necklace—yours, Lady Hightone—was in the pocket of one of Mr. Dauntless' jackets.

DAVID: This is ridiculous. I never had a necklace of any kind in any jacket.

HUMPHREY: I was getting my own jacket from the clothes rack in the south hall. Inadvertently, I knocked Mr. Dauntless' jacket to the floor. The necklace fell from his pocket. (*Dramatically*) Dauntless, you are a wolf in sheep's clothing, taking advantage of the hospitality of this house by playing the role of a dastardly thief.

DIANA: I just don't believe it.

REGGIE: Doesn't sound like you, Dauntless, old boy—something jolly fishy about this.

DAVID: I assure you I haven't the slightest idea of how the necklace ever got into my pocket.

LADY HIGHTONE: A thief! A common robber! So, Mr. Dauntless, at last you are revealed for the low, ungrateful creature you really are. I repeat what I have said. Leave this house at once! I shall not call in Scotland Yard, but not, I assure you, out of any affection for you. I should not want the scandal involved. The Hightone name must be protected at all costs!

DIANA: Oh, Mother, I know there must be some mistake. David would never descend to such a low act. He—

LADY HIGHTONE: He is a common rascal. And the sooner he is removed from your life, the better.

LADY CLARA: After all, this is all merely circumstantial evidence, Letitia—

LADY HIGHTONE (*Haughtily*): Clara, do me the favor of allowing me to make the important decisions in my own home.

REGGIE: But Mater, we must use reason in these matters. Everything is so frightfully vague and—

LADY HIGHTONE: And as for you, Reggie, all you've done is chatter aimlessly since you arose this morning. Be quiet! (*To* DAVID) Mr. Dauntless, you may now take your leave! And be thankful that you are not destined to see the inside of a good, substantial English prison. We know how to deal with confirmed criminals on this side of the water!

DAVID (*Protesting*): But I want to clear my name. I must—

LADY HIGHTONE (*Contemptuously*): Your name? Dauntless? Hmmph! A name like that, since it means nothing and stands for nothing, can hardly be worth clearing. We have the word of the Earl of Feefum's son that you are a thief!

DIANA: You had better go, David. (*Sadly*) All this is hopeless. (*Impetuously* DAVID *goes to* DIANA *and embraces her.*)

DAVID: I shall return, darling. And I shall never cease fighting for what is right.

LADY HIGHTONE: Unhand my daughter! (DAVID *kisses* DIANA.) Shameless! Shameless!

DAVID: Goodbye, my love. (*He goes toward center door.*) And don't give up hope. (*He exits.* DIANA *begins to sob and rushes off weeping.*)

LADY CLARA: I hope you're not making a bad mistake, Letitia.

LADY HIGHTONE: I am never mistaken.

REGGIE (*Trying to restore some degree of good cheer*): Well, this is a jolly morning for riding, so I shall be off on the old gray mare.

LADY CLARA: I think I shall accompany you, Reggie. A breath of fresh air is what I need after these sordid proceedings.

REGGIE: Then—to horse! What ho and pip-pip. See you later. Come, Aunt Clara. (REGGIE *and* AUNT CLARA *exit.*)

HUMPHREY: I am genuinely sorry, Lady Hightone, to have been the unwitting cause of so distasteful a scene.

LADY HIGHTONE: Don't be sorry, Humphrey. Actually, you have performed a great service. You have given me one more reason to rid the household of a person who was most unwelcome.

HUMPHREY: A most common and untrustworthy fellow, Lady Hightone.

LADY HIGHTONE: Common, indeed. But the important thing is that now you will have Diana to yourself. Frankly, I have been disappointed in you, Humphrey. You haven't been making much progress. But now that this Dauntless person has been revealed for the insufferable cad he is, you have a glorious opportunity.

HUMPHREY: It has been most difficult, Lady Hightone. Since the intrusion on the scene by that American thief,

I have had no chance at all of being alone with Diana. It has been extremely frustrating.

LADY HIGHTONE (*Firmly*): Things will change now. You should sweep her off her feet. She is, after all, my daughter, so she is, essentially, a sensible girl. But you must assert yourself. A girl likes a man to be in command of the situation.

HUMPHREY: I'll do my best.

LADY HIGHTONE: How is Sir Hilary progressing with his writing?

HUMPHREY: He has been a bit balky this morning. He keeps saying he should be with Angus, the gardener. I have finally persuaded him to get to work, though.

LADY HIGHTONE: Splendid. I don't know what we'd do without you, Humphrey.

HUMPHREY (*Obsequiously*): I try to be of service. (SIR HILARY *suddenly appears, walking on tiptoe, and obviously trying to get past* LADY HIGHTONE *and* HUMPHREY. *When he is halfway across stage,* LADY HIGHTONE *catches sight of him.*)

LADY HIGHTONE: Hilary!

SIR HILARY: Er—yes, my dear.

LADY HIGHTONE: Just where do you think you're going?

SIR HILARY: Going? Ah, yes, to be sure, going.

LADY HIGHTONE: You're not going to the garden. You've work to do, and you're going to do it.

SIR HILARY: Just taking a breather, my dear. Writing's hard on a man—deucedly hard. Need a breath of air.

LADY HIGHTONE (*Imperiously*): Return to the study at once! Mr. Witherspoon will accompany you.

SIR HILARY: Witherspoon? Oh, Witherspoon. Thought you had left for the day.

HUMPHREY (*Brightly*): Not at all, Sir Hilary. I'm more than anxious to get back to work. (HUMPHREY *goes to center exit.*) I'm ready, Sir Hilary. Shall we continue our communing with the Muses?

LADY HIGHTONE: Run along, Hilary. (*She casts a conspiratorial smile at* HUMPHREY.) And remember, Humphrey, assert yourself.

HUMPHREY (*Returning the smile*): I will, Lady Hightone. (*He and* SIR HILARY *exit.* CLOVERBLOOM *enters to clear dishes from serving table.*)

LADY HIGHTONE (*With an air of great satisfaction*): Cloverbloom, there will be one less place for luncheon. The despicable Mr. Dauntless, I am happy to say, is now among the missing. (*She smiles complacently as the curtain closes.*)

CURTAIN

* * * *

SCENE 2

TIME: *One week later, in the afternoon.*

SETTING: *The same as Scene 1. The dishes are cleared away; only a vase of flowers stands on table.*

AT RISE: REGGIE *stands at center of stage, whistling a tune.* DIANA, *looking very dejected, enters through center door.*

DIANA (*Dully*): Hello, Reggie.

REGGIE: Hello, old girl. You seem gloomy.

DIANA: I am. Wouldn't you be?

REGGIE: Suppose I would, old bean, suppose I would. When the mater is on the warpath, things do get a bit uncomfortable. Have you heard from David?

DIANA: He sent me a note. He has a room at the George and Crown.

REGGIE: He has my sympathy. The food is frightful there. The mutton is like leather, and the soup tastes like turpentine. He deserves better than that. I still can't believe he's a thief.

DIANA (*Angrily*): Of course, he isn't!

REGGIE: Don't lose your temper, old thing. I have faith in him, too. Though it was a sad day when that Witherspoon discovered the pearls. Hanging about you a good deal this past week, isn't he?

DIANA: I can't escape him. When he's not with Father in the study, he's with me. I just can't bear him!

REGGIE: He has a personality only a mother could love. But, as the French so rightly put it, *c'est la vie.* (*Going toward center exit*) Well, what ho and pip-pip. Must change for dinner. See you anon. (REGGIE *exits.* DIANA *sits mournfully on settee, the picture of dejection.* HUMPHREY *enters. He catches sight of* DIANA *and is obviously pleased.*)

HUMPHREY: Hello.

DIANA (*Looking up coldly*): Hello, Humphrey. (HUMPHREY *sits beside her.*) Aren't you supposed to be working with Father?

HUMPHREY: He's at work on the notes I arranged for him this morning.

DIANA: Poor dear.

HUMPHREY: Oh, I don't mind doing it. It's all part of the job.

DIANA (*Coldly*): I don't mean you. I mean Father.

HUMPHREY: Oh. (*Recovering quickly*) There's something I've been wanting to talk to you about.

DIANA: I really don't feel like talking to you right now, Humphrey.

HUMPHREY: I know how you feel. You've been disillusioned by that monstrous Dauntless.

DIANA: He isn't monstrous!

HUMPHREY: Diana, I think it is wonderful of you to be so loyal. It is a quality in you that I admire tremendously. But we must face facts. The man is a common thief—

DIANA (*Rising*): Please, Humphrey, if you're going to continue in this vein, you may leave at once.

HUMPHREY (*Penitently*): I'm sorry, Diana. Please sit down. Let us forget about Dauntless. What I wish to speak of is more personal and concerns us both. (*Gathering his courage*) Er—er, Diana, you are aware, of course, that my father is the Earl of Feefum.

DIANA: I am.

HUMPHREY: And that I have certain prospects. After all, mine is an old and distinguished family. (*Generously*) And so is yours.

DIANA: None of this is exactly news to me.

HUMPHREY: Surely, you must have observed that I feel a warm affection for you. (*Hurriedly*) In fact, if I may be blunt, I worship the ground on which you walk.

DIANA: Really, Humphrey, I have no interest in you at all.

HUMPHREY (*Moving closer to her*): People like us were made for each other. We have the same breeding, the same outlook on life, the same—oh, Diana. (*He grasps her and attempts to kiss her just as* DAVID *enters center.* DIANA *struggles in* HUMPHREY's *grasp.* DAVID *comes to settee, lifts* HUMPHREY *by the collar, gets him to his feet, and then knocks him over with a well-aimed blow.*)

DIANA: David, darling!

DAVID: I couldn't stay away any longer. That inn is like a dungeon. I had to see you. (SIR HILARY *enters center and comes quickly to settee.*)

SIR HILARY: Bless my soul! What is this? (*Peering near-sightedly* at HUMPHREY, *who is sitting on the floor holding his jaw and moaning*) Why, it's Witherspoon! Capital! Capital! Who did it?

DIANA: David struck him when Humphrey tried to kiss me.

SIR HILARY (*Pumping* DAVID'S *hand*): Splendid, my boy! Splendid! Wanted to do it for weeks myself. (LADY HIGHTONE *enters.*)

DAVID (*Earnestly*): I'm sorry, my lady, but I simply had to see Diana again. And I must insist on the opportunity to clear the Dauntless name of suspicion.

LADY HIGHTONE: Suspicion, indeed! Humphrey brought us proof of your guilt.

HUMPHREY (*Rising from floor rubbing his jaw*): You blasted Americans are all savages!

DIANA (*Heatedly*): Don't be calling other people savages when you've been acting like a caveman yourself.

SIR HILARY (*As* LADY CLARA *and* REGGIE *appear*): Can't have young whelps of secretaries going around kissing my daughter. Simply not done these days. Just isn't cricket.

REGGIE: Right-ho, Pater.

LADY CLARA: Mr. Dauntless and Diana made such a lovely couple!

DIANA: Then why is Mother trying to spoil our happiness?

LADY HIGHTONE (*Shrieking*): Will you all be quiet! I want to know the meaning of this. (*To* HUMPHREY) What is wrong with your jaw, Humphrey?

HUMPHREY: He hit me—and without warning. And I wear glasses.

LADY HIGHTONE: How vile! How deceitful! How thoroughly American! I shall have the police take care of you this time, Mr. Dauntless. I can see I was too lenient with you the first time!

Sir Hilary: Now, look here, my dear—

Lady Hightone: Be quiet!

Sir Hilary (*Weakly*): Yes, my dear. (Cloverbloom *appears in center doorway.*)

Cloverbloom: Mr. and Mrs. Harvey Dauntless.

Lady Hightone: Dauntless! (Mr. *and* Mrs. Harvey Dauntless *enter briskly.* Mr. Dauntless *is carrying a large, black notebook under his arm.*)

David: Mother! Father! (*He kisses his mother and shakes his father's hand.*)

Mr. Dauntless: As soon as we got your cablegram, we hopped a plane and here we are. First, we had your letter about the fine little girl you'd met. (*He grins at* Diana.) And a right purty filly she is. But we were troubled when you said her mother didn't think you were good enough for her. Yes, sir, that was a real blow to the pride and good name of the Dauntless family.

Mrs. Dauntless: And then that terrible cable, David. Imagine your being accused of theft! I never heard of such a thing.

Sir Hilary (*Emerging from his fog*): Dauntless? Dauntless? The boy's parents? How do you do? (*He shakes hands cordially with* Mr. *and* Mrs. Dauntless.)

Lady Hightone: That will do, Hilary. This is scarcely the time or place for any display of hospitality. Your son, sir and madam, is a thief and a ruffian. He not only stole my pearls, but he has just savagely attacked my husband's secretary.

Mr. Dauntless (*Menacingly*): So you're the guy who said my son is a thief, hey? (*Advancing on* Humphrey) For two cents, I'd pin your ears back.

Mrs. Dauntless (*As* Humphrey *retreats*): Harvey! Harvey! Remember your blood pressure.

LADY HIGHTONE: The young man you are threatening, Mr. Dauntless, is beyond reproach. We have his word that your son is a criminal, and that is all that is needed. After all, Mr. Witherspoon is the Earl of Feefum's son. Consequently, his word is beyond doubt.

MR. DAUNTLESS: I don't care if his father is the Prince of Wales. My son is no thief!

MRS. DAUNTLESS: Blood pressure, Harvey, blood pressure!

DAVID: Lady Hightone, I've had a week to think about all this. And I'd like to ask you a question. Where are your pearls usually kept?

REGGIE: I can answer that, old bean. Mater always keeps them in the wall safe in the library, with Pater's notes, a few family heirlooms, and all that sort of rot.

LADY HIGHTONE: Speak only when you're spoken to, Reggie.

DIANA: Reggie's right, though. You haven't worn those pearls since the County Ball. They must have been in the safe.

DAVID: And who knows the combination of the safe?

LADY CLARA: Not many, I can tell you. That combination is the best-kept secret of the ages.

REGGIE: Hear! Hear!

SIR HILARY: Combination? Safe? I know it. Letitia knows it. And Witherspoon, of course.

DAVID (*Triumphantly*): Exactly!

REGGIE: Oh, I say, old bean, I see what you mean. Impossible for you to get at the safe, what?

DAVID: I certainly don't know the combination. But Humphrey Witherspoon does.

HUMPHREY (*Heatedly*): Are you insinuating—

CLOVERBLOOM (*Who has remained silent in doorway, suddenly coughs*): Ahem! May I say a word, m'lady?

LADY HIGHTONE: What is it, Cloverbloom?

CLOVERBLOOM: I have remained silent until now not wishing to intrude in family business. But a week ago, I saw Mr. Witherspoon emerge from the library, with the pearls in his hand.

DIANA: Oh, Cloverbloom. Exactly when was this?

CLOVERBLOOM: On the day that Mr. David left us.

DAVID (*Advancing on* HUMPHREY): You tried to frame me then, Witherspoon.

HUMPHREY: This is preposterous—I—

DIANA: You look guilty, Humphrey.

REGGIE: Like a jolly old criminal—

LADY CLARA: No question about it—

SIR HILARY: This is the end, Witherspoon. I'll write you a check for your services up to date. And then it's off with you.

DAVID: Are you convinced, Lady Hightone? (HUMPHREY *creeps toward exit.* DIANA *goes after him.*)

DIANA: Just a moment, Humphrey. (HUMPHREY *turns, and* DIANA *slaps his face.* HUMPHREY *exits angrily.*) Now I feel better.

REGGIE: Bravo!

LADY CLARA: Well done, my child.

LADY HIGHTONE: Conduct that scarcely becomes a lady, Diana. But nothing is changed. (*To* DAVID) You may not be a criminal, but you are still common.

MR. DAUNTLESS: I take it, Lady Hightone, that in addition to accusing my son falsely, you also object to him as a suitor for your daughter's hand?

LADY HIGHTONE: You are correct in your assumptions. The entire affair is impossible.

MR. DAUNTLESS: Not good enough, I suppose, to mingle with the Hightones?

LADY HIGHTONE: Exactly.

MRS. DAUNTLESS: Read from your notebook, Harvey.

MR. DAUNTLESS: That's just what I'm going to do. (*He holds up his notebook.*) Now, Lady Hightone, I'm going to give you some nice tidbits of information. You say you don't think the Dauntlesses are good enough for the Hightones. Well, let me tell you, I'm not so sure the Hightones are good enough to mingle with the Dauntlesses.

LADY HIGHTONE: Mr. Dauntless, not only are your manners deplorable, but I suspect you of incipient insanity.

MR. DAUNTLESS: Don't kid yourself, madam. I'm not off my trolley.

LADY HIGHTONE: That remains to be seen.

MR. DAUNTLESS: When David wrote me that you were treating him like a coyote and putting obstacles between him and this fine little lady here, I decided to take steps. I did a little research on my own.

MRS. DAUNTLESS: And a very thorough job you did, Harvey.

MR. DAUNTLESS: You bet I was thorough. Let me tell you some of the pleasant little items I've found out about the Hightone family.

LADY CLARA: This should be most interesting.

MR. DAUNTLESS (*Reading from notebook*): Sir Gregory Hightone. 1568–1601. Beheaded for treason by the order of Queen Elizabeth I.

LADY HIGHTONE: Now see here, Mr. Dauntless—

MR. DAUNTLESS: Please, madam. This is just the beginning. (*Reading again from notebook*) Lord Sebastian Hightone. 1695–1745. Kicked out of his regiment for cheating at cards. Nice fellow, that. Here's another. Quagmire Hightone, better known as "Soapy," married a Gypsy girl in 1832, served seven years at Dartmoor for a jewel robbery. Madam, I'm a bit disturbed that my son might want to become a member by marriage of a family that boasts card sharpers and thieves.

DAVID: Now, Dad, don't be hasty.

MR. DAUNTLESS (*Still reading from notebook*): Now here's a real humdinger. Cutlass Harry Hightone, the most notorious pirate of the 17th Century— (LADY HIGHTONE *goes to settee and sits weakly.*)

REGGIE: Oh, I say, Mater, you're not ill, are you? (*The usually staid* CLOVERBLOOM *has begun to giggle.*)

LADY HIGHTONE (*Recovering*): You may leave, Cloverbloom.

CLOVERBLOOM (*Trying to suppress his giggling*): V-very, good, m-m'lady. (*He exits.*)

MRS. DAUNTLESS: I think you've said enough, Harvey.

MR. DAUNTLESS: Well, all this talk about the Dauntlesses not being good enough for the Hightones just got my dander up.

LADY HIGHTONE (*Turning on* SIR HILARY): And you, Hilary, have let him malign our family, our sacred heritage. Surely, you have something to say to this Yankee upstart and his absurd accusations.

SIR HILARY: Well, you see, my dear, there's really nothing I can say.

LADY HIGHTONE: Nothing you can say! Well, I can, and furthermore I—

SIR HILARY (*Interrupting*): But, my dear, it's all true—every dashed bit. When I did all my reading for the family history, I discovered it all.

LADY HIGHTONE (*Faintly*): You mean it's all true.

SIR HILARY: Indeed it is and a good deal more that Mr. Dauntless is too much of a gentleman to reveal. That's why I never wanted to go on with the book about the family—

REGGIE: Don't blame you, old boy.

LADY HIGHTONE (*Rising*): Well, perhaps we can discuss this further. But none of this has anything to do, Mr. Dauntless, with the fact that you are engaged in trade, in manufacturing dog food, of all things. And as if that isn't enough, I am sure your son would be unable to support Diana in the manner to which she is accustomed.

MR. DAUNTLESS: That, madam, is the laugh of the day.

MRS. DAUNTLESS: It is funny, isn't it, Harvey?

LADY HIGHTONE: What do you mean?

MR. DAUNTLESS: Do you know how much money my dog food company grossed last year? Well, let me tell you. We did eighteen million dollars worth of business.

REGGIE: Oh, I say, that's a nice round sum!

MR. DAUNTLESS: At a conservative estimate, I'd say—and I'm not trying to brag, mind you—that I am worth in the neighborhood of five million dollars.

LADY CLARA: And that's a very nice neighborhood.

LADY HIGHTONE: Five million dollars!

MR. DAUNTLESS: At a conservative estimate. And it will all be David's some day.

MRS. DAUNTLESS: Tell her about your decoration, Harvey.

MR. DAUNTLESS: Good idea. (*He takes from his pocket a large medal with a ribbon on it.*) Look here, madam. (LADY HIGHTONE *examines it.*) That is the Order of the Six Palms of the British Empire. Presented to me personally by your own Queen.

REGGIE: Long live the Queen!

LADY HIGHTONE: The Order of the Six Palms!

MR. DAUNTLESS: None other. Presented for services during World War II. We found out that dog food, with a couple of things added, was ideal for humans, too. Why, half your British Empire was eating modified Dauntless' Puppo at one time.

REGGIE: Woof! Woof!

MR. DAUNTLESS: Furthermore, I'm a generous man. I'm willing to let bygones be bygones. After seeing this pretty young girl here, (*He smiles at* DIANA.) I think she and David would make a dandy couple.

REGGIE: Hear! Hear!

SIR HILARY: Couple? Yes, indeed. Ideal couple, to be sure.

LADY CLARA: I'm with you, Mr. Dauntless.

MRS. DAUNTLESS: So am I, Harvey.

REGGIE: It's your move, Mater.

LADY CLARA: And make it the right one, Letitia.

LADY HIGHTONE (*Coming to* DAVID *and* DIANA): Five million dollars! The Order of the Six Palms! (*She pauses, and then joins* DAVID'S *and* DIANA'S *hands. She speaks dramatically.*) Bless you, my children!

REGGIE: This is the gladdest day of all the glad new year.

LADY CLARA: Letitia, you're a bit of all right.

LADY HIGHTONE: Perhaps I was a trifle hasty in my judgment of this dear boy. (DAVID *and* DIANA *embrace ecstatically.*)

SIR HILARY: Capital! Capital! Let's all have tea.

MR. DAUNTLESS: Just to show there are no ill feelings, Lady Hightone, I will drink a cup of tea. I hate the stuff, but I'm willing to do what I can to cement relations with the British Empire.

MRS. DAUNTLESS: Good for you, Harvey.

SIR HILARY (*Rather slyly*): Of course, my dear, I should be at work on the book.

LADY HIGHTONE: Hilary, forget the book. Burn what you've already written. Go out and enjoy your roses.

SIR HILARY: Burn? Roses? (*He rushes to door, exits, shouting*) Cloverbloom! A box of matches!

LADY CLARA: This is a happy day for all. Hilary doesn't

have to write his book, David has Diana, Witherspoon has gone. Everything is as right as right in this best of all possible worlds.

REGGIE (*Grasping* LADY CLARA's *waist and dancing with her*): Aunt Clara, you have just uttered the speech of the age! What-ho, pip-pip, and ta-ta! Three jolly cheers, for hearts, flowers, and Little Creek, Wyoming! (*All cheer and laugh.* DAVID *and* DIANA *again embrace, the others regarding the couple with delight as the curtains close.*)

THE END

Production Notes

WHAT HO!

Characters: 6 male; 4 female.

Playing Time: 35 minutes.

Costumes: Lady Hightone wears a flowing dressing gown in Scene 1, and a similar type of costume for Scene 2; she always carries a lorgnette. Sir Hilary wears a high winged collar with an old-fashioned cravat and vest. Reggie Hightone wears riding clothes. Diana Hightone wears an attractive dress. Lady Clara is dressed in British tweeds. Cloverbloom wears a typical butler's costume. Humphrey Witherspoon wears spectacles, a dark gray suit and vest. David Dauntless carries a cane in Scene 1, wears slacks and sport jacket. Mr. Dauntless wears a business suit. Mrs. Dauntless wears a traveling suit, hat, and carries handbag and gloves.

Properties: Several covered dishes, silver casseroles, etc.; breakfast dishes and pot of tea; cane for David; spectacles and pearl necklace for Humphrey; notebook and large medal with ribbon for Mr. Dauntless; vase of flowers.

Setting: Scene 1: The terrace of Sir Hilary Hightone's country home in England. At upstage center is a door leading into the house. At center is a large table set for breakfast. At left and right of table are chairs. At downstage right and left are settees. All the furniture is of the outdoor type. On a sidetable, at left of center exit, are various covered dishes, silver casseroles, and the like.

Scene 2: The same as Scene 1, except that the breakfast dishes are cleared away. Only a vase of flowers now stands on the table.

Lighting: No special effects.